Core Books in Advanced Mathematics

GW00361145

Differentiation

Core Books in Advanced Mathematics

General Editor: C. PLUMPTON, Moderator in Mathematics,
University of London School Examinations Department;
formerly Reader in Engineering Mathematics,
Queen Mary College, University of London.

Advisory Editor: N. WARWICK

Titles available

Differentiation
Integration
Vectors
Curve Sketching

Core Books in Advanced Mathematics

Differentiation

C. T. Moss
Formerly Chief Examiner and Moderator in Advanced Level
Mathematics, AEB; Senior Lecturer and Deputy Head of
Mathematics, The City University, London.

C. Plumpton
Moderator in Mathematics, University of
London School Examinations Department;
formerly Reader in Engineering Mathematics,
Queen Mary College, University of London.

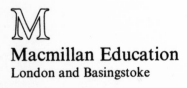

Macmillan Education
London and Basingstoke

© C. T. Moss and C. Plumpton 1983

All rights reserved. No part of this publication
may be reproduced or transmitted, in any form or
by any means, without permission.

First published 1983

Published by
Macmillan Education Limited
Houndmills Basingstoke Hampshire RG21 2XS
and London
Associated companies throughout the world

Typeset in Hong Kong by Asco Trade Typesetting Ltd.
Printed in Hong Kong

British Library Cataloguing in Publication Data
Moss, C. T.
Differentiation – (Core books in advanced mathematics)
1. Calculus, Differential
I. Title   II. Plumpton, Charles
III. Series
515.3′3   QA304
ISBN 0-333-31794-7

Contents

Preface

Advanced level mathematics syllabuses are once again undergoing changes of content and approach, following the revolution in the early 1960s which led to the unfortunate dichotomy between 'modern' and 'traditional' mathematics. The current trend in syllabuses for Advanced level mathematics now being developed and published by many GCE Boards is towards an integrated approach, taking the best of the topics and approaches of the modern and traditional, in an attempt to create a realistic examination target, through syllabuses which are maximal for examining and minimal for teaching. In addition, resulting from a number of initiatives, core syllabuses are being developed for Advanced level mathematics syllabuses, consisting of techniques of pure mathematics as taught in schools and colleges at this level.

The concept of a core can be used in several ways, one of which is mentioned above, namely the idea of a core syllabus to which options such as theoretical mechanics, further pure mathematics and statistics can be added. The books in this series are core books involving a different use of the core idea. They are books on a range of topics, each of which is central to the study of Advanced level mathematics; they form small core studies of their own, of topics which together cover the main areas of any single-subject mathematics syllabus at Advanced level.

Particularly at times when economic conditions make the problems of acquiring comprehensive textbooks giving complete syllabus coverage acute, schools and colleges and individual students can collect as many of the core books as they need, one or more, to supplement books already possessed, so that the most recent syllabuses of, for example, the London, Cambridge, AEB and JMB GCE Boards, can be covered at minimum expense. Alternatively, of course, the whole set of core books give complete syllabus coverage of single-subject Advanced level mathematics syllabuses.

The aim of each book is to develop a major topic of the single-subject syllabuses, giving essential book work and worked examples and exercises arising from the authors' vast experience of examining at this level and including actual past GCE questions also. Thus, as well as using the core books in either of the above ways, they would also be ideal for supplementing comprehensive textbooks in the sense of providing more examples and exercises, so necessary for preparation and revision for examinations on the Advanced level mathematics syllabuses offered by the GCE Boards.

In this book on differentiation, it has been assumed that the reader has a rudimentary knowledge of calculus. Consequently, whilst the basic results and general theorems on differentiation are given, no attempt has been made to prove them. The writers' main concern has been to try to ensure that, given basic results and general theorems, the readers can by (i) following the numerous worked examples and (ii) working out for themselves the frequent complementary exercises, be enabled to cope easily with all such examination questions to be found in the GCE A-level papers. It is also believed that many first-year university and polytechnic engineering and applied science students will find the text a most helpful aid in ensuring proficiency in differentiation and its applications. In an attempt to establish good techniques, the opportunity has been taken of drawing the reader's attention to quicker and better solutions whenever appropriate.

Approximately half of the book is devoted to the many applications of differential calculus.

The authors are grateful to the following GCE Examining Boards for permission to reproduce questions from past Advanced Level GCE papers: University of London Entrance and School Examinations Council (L); The Associated Examining Board (AEB).

C. T. Moss
C. Plumpton

1 Basic techniques

1.1 Gradients

An equation, such as $y = 10x^2$, expresses a relationship between two variables x and y. When $x = 1$ then $y = 10.1^2 = 10$. When $x = 2$ then $y = 10.2^2 = 40$. When $x = 3$ then $y = 90$ and so on. In fact, when x is given a value, the corresponding value of y can be found by squaring that value and multiplying by 10, i.e. the value of y depends upon the value of x.

We say that y is a function of x and in general write $y = f(x)$ or $y = F(x)$, the f or F being short for 'function of'.

As we deal with many different functions and must distinguish between them, we sometimes use letters other than f or F, e.g. we often write $y = y(x)$ or $y = \phi(x)$ to mention just two alternative notations.

If we obtain a set of pairs of related values of x and y, i.e. (x, y), we can plot these on a diagram and obtain a graph of the function.

For $y = 10x^2$ we have $(x, y) \equiv (0, 0), (1, 10), (2, 40), (3, 90), (-1, 10), (-2, 40), (-3, 90)$, and plotting the points we obtain the graph shown in Fig. 1.1, where $A \equiv (1, 10)$, $B \equiv (2, 40)$, $C \equiv (3, 90)$, $P \equiv (2, 10)$ and $Q \equiv (3, 10)$.

As x increases from 1 to 3, y increases from 10 to 90. If x represents time in hours and y represents distance in kilometres, then, in the two hour interval, a distance of $90 - 10 = 80$ km is covered. This gives the *average* speed during *this* interval of time as $80/2 = 40$ km h^{-1}. The figure 40 is also the tangent of angle CAQ, which is said to be the *gradient* of the chord AC.

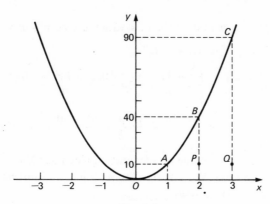

Fig. 1.1

In the one hour interval from $x = 1$ to $x = 2$ the distance y increases from 10 to 40 km. In *this* one hour interval the *average* speed is $(40 - 10)/1$, or $30 \, \mathrm{km \, h^{-1}}$; 30 also being the tangent of the angle BAP and therefore the slope of the chord AB.

To find the actual or exact speed at any instant, we have to make the time interval so small that there is no time to accelerate or retard. We have to consider, therefore, what happens to ratios such as BP/AP as AP is made smaller and smaller. Clearly the gradient of the chord AB will successively become the gradient of the chords AB_1, AB_2, AB_3, as shown in Fig. 1.2, until ultimately as P reaches A the chord will become the tangent to the curve at the point A. The gradient of this tangent then represents the actual speed, in $\mathrm{km \, h^{-1}}$, at the time $x = 1$ hour.

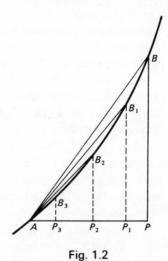

Fig. 1.2

To calculate the actual gradient of the tangent to $y = 10x^2$ we proceed as follows:

Let x increase to $x + h$, and let the new value of y be $y + k$ so that

$$y + k = 10(x + h)^2$$

$$\Rightarrow \frac{\text{increase in } y}{\text{increase in } x} = \frac{(y + k) - y}{(x + h) - x} = \frac{10(x + h)^2 - 10x^2}{h}$$

$$= \frac{10x^2 + 20xh + 10h^2 - 10x^2}{h} = 20x + 10h.$$

When the increase h in x is made smaller and smaller, then $20x + 10h$ approaches nearer and nearer to $20x$. We say that $20x + 10h$ has a limiting value of $20x$ as h decreases to zero and we write

$$\lim_{h \to 0} (20x + 10h) = 20x.$$

When $x = 1$, $20x = 20$ and therefore the actual speed when $x = 1$ hour is 20 km h^{-1}.

1.2 Increment notation

Instead of using h for a small increase in the variable x, an alternative and often more convenient notation is to use δx (delta x). It must never be taken or read as δ multiplied by x; the δ and the x are inseparable. δx must always be read as 'a small increase in x'.

Likewise we write $k \equiv \delta y$, a small increase in y. In this notation the above argument would read:

If $y = 10x^2$, let x increase by a small amount δx and let the corresponding increment in y be δy. Then the new value of y is $y + \delta y$, where

$$y + \delta y = 10(x + \delta x)^2.$$

Subtracting

$$\Rightarrow \delta y = 10(x + \delta x)^2 - 10x^2$$

$$= 20x \cdot \delta x + 10(\delta x)^2$$

$$\Rightarrow \frac{\delta y}{\delta x} = 20x + 10\delta x$$

$$\Rightarrow \lim_{\delta x \to 0} \frac{\delta y}{\delta x} = \lim_{\delta x \to 0} (20x + 10\delta x) = 20x.$$

This process, for a function $y[= f(x)]$, of finding the ratio of the incremental change δy in y to the incremental change δx in x and then obtaining the limiting value of this ratio as δx tends to zero is known as 'differentiation from first principles'. The answer is denoted by the symbol $\frac{dy}{dx}$ and it is called the *derived function* or the *derivative* of y with respect to x (abbreviated to w.r. to x).

It must be clearly understood that $\frac{dy}{dx}$ is a notation; it is not a fraction in which the dy can be separated from the dx. In fact $\frac{dy}{dx}$ or $\frac{d}{dx}(y)$ is the result of the operation of taking the limit of $\frac{\delta y}{\delta x}$ as $\delta x \to 0$.

1.3 Derivatives

We can find the derivatives of some elementary functions by actually calculating the limit, i.e. by differentiating from first principles. However, by using a few general theorems (quoted below) and a few simple results we can easily and quickly determine derivatives of quite complicated functions.

The known results which are usually calculated from first principles are given in the following table.

y	$\dfrac{dy}{dx}$
c, a constant	0
x^n	nx^{n-1} for all $n \neq 0$
$\sin x$	$\cos x$
$\cos x$	$-\sin x$
$\ln x$	$\dfrac{1}{x}$
e^x	e^x

We shall take these as proved but the reader may, if desired, find the proofs in another book.

1.4 General theorems on differentiation

THEOREM I   If $u = f(x)$ and $y = cu = cf(x)$, where c is a constant, then $\dfrac{dy}{dx} = c\dfrac{du}{dx}$.

Example 1

(i) $y = 7x^4 \Rightarrow \dfrac{dy}{dx} = 7 \cdot 4x^3 = 28x^3,$

(ii) $y = 9 \sin \theta \Rightarrow \dfrac{dy}{d\theta} = 9 \cos \theta,$

(iii) $v = 2 \ln t \Rightarrow \dfrac{dv}{dt} = 2 \cdot \dfrac{1}{t} = \dfrac{2}{t},$

(iv) $y = \dfrac{3}{x^2} = 3x^{-2} \Rightarrow \dfrac{dy}{dx} = 3(-2)x^{-3} = \dfrac{-6}{x^3}.$

THEOREM II   If u and v are functions of x and $y = u \pm v$, then

$$\frac{dy}{dx} = \frac{du}{dx} \pm \frac{dv}{dx}.$$

More generally, if $y = u_1 \pm u_2 \pm u_3 \pm u_4 \pm \ldots \pm u_n$, then

$$\frac{dy}{dx} = \frac{du_1}{dx} \pm \frac{du_2}{dx} \pm \frac{du_3}{dx} \pm \frac{du_4}{dx} \pm \ldots \pm \frac{du_n}{dx}.$$

Example 2

(i) $y = 3x^4 + 4 \sin x \Rightarrow \dfrac{dy}{dx} = 12x^3 + 4 \cos x,$

(ii) $y = 2e^t + 3 \cos t \Rightarrow \dfrac{dy}{dt} = 2e^t - 3 \sin t,$

(iii) $y = \dfrac{1}{x^2} - 2 \ln x \Rightarrow \dfrac{dy}{dx} = \dfrac{-2}{x^3} - \dfrac{2}{x}.$

THEOREM III If u and v are functions of x and $y = uv$, then

$$\frac{dy}{dx} = u\frac{dv}{dx} + v\frac{du}{dx}.$$

More generally, if $y = u_1 . u_2 . u_3 . u_4 \ldots u_n$, then

$$\frac{dy}{dx} = \frac{du_1}{dx}.u_2.u_3 \ldots u_n + u_1.\frac{du_2}{dx}.u_3.u_4 \ldots u_n$$

$$+ u_1.u_2.\frac{du_3}{dx}.u_4 \ldots u_n + \ldots + \ldots + u_1.u_2.u_3 \ldots u_{n-1}.\frac{du_n}{dx}.$$

Example 3

(i) $y = x^3 . \ln x \Rightarrow \dfrac{dy}{dx} = x^3 . \dfrac{1}{x} + 3x^2 \ln x,$

$\qquad\quad u \quad v \qquad\qquad\quad u \quad \dfrac{dv}{dx} \quad v \quad \dfrac{du}{dx}$

(ii) $y = \cos\theta . \sin\theta \Rightarrow \dfrac{dy}{d\theta} = \cos\theta(\cos\theta) + \sin\theta(-\sin\theta)$

$$= \cos^2\theta - \sin^2\theta = \cos 2\theta,$$

(iii) $y = \sqrt{x}\,e^x \Rightarrow \dfrac{dy}{dx} = \sqrt{x}.e^x + e^x.\dfrac{1}{2}x^{-1/2} = e^x\left[\sqrt{x} + \dfrac{1}{2\sqrt{x}}\right],$

(iv) $y = (1 - 3t^2) \sin t \Rightarrow \dfrac{dy}{dt} = (1 - 3t^2).\cos t + (-6t) \sin t$

$$= (1 - 3t^2) \cos t - 6t \sin t,$$

(v) $y = x^2 e^x \sin x \Rightarrow \dfrac{dy}{dx} = 2x.e^x.\sin x + x^2.e^x.\sin x + x^2.e^x.\cos x.$

THEOREM IV If u and v are functions of x and $y = \dfrac{u}{v}$, then

$$\frac{dy}{dx} = \frac{v\dfrac{du}{dx} - u\dfrac{dv}{dx}}{v^2}.$$

This result can be obtained from the product rule. For if $y = u/v$, then $u = y.v$. Since u and v are functions of x, then $y = u/v$ is also a function of x.

Using the product rule (Theorem III) for $u = yv \Rightarrow \dfrac{du}{dx} = y\dfrac{dv}{dx} + v\dfrac{dy}{dx}$.

Rearranging, $\qquad\qquad v\dfrac{dy}{dx} = \dfrac{du}{dx} - y\dfrac{dv}{dx}$

or $\qquad \dfrac{dy}{dx} = \dfrac{1}{v}\left(\dfrac{du}{dx} - \dfrac{u}{v}\dfrac{dv}{dx}\right) = \dfrac{v\dfrac{du}{dx} - u\dfrac{dv}{dx}}{v^2}\qquad$ since $\quad y = \dfrac{u}{v}$.

Example 4

(i) $y = \dfrac{x^2}{1 + x^3} \Rightarrow \dfrac{dy}{dx} = \dfrac{(1 + x^3).2x - x^2.3x^2}{(1 + x^3)^2} = \dfrac{2x - x^4}{(1 + x^3)^2}$,

(ii) $y = \tan x = \dfrac{\sin x}{\cos x} \Rightarrow \dfrac{dy}{dx} = \dfrac{\cos x . \cos x - \sin x(-\sin x)}{\cos^2 x}$

$\Rightarrow \dfrac{dy}{dx} = \dfrac{\cos^2 x + \sin^2 x}{\cos^2 x} = \dfrac{1}{\cos^2 x} = \sec^2 x$, since $\cos^2 x + \sin^2 x = 1$,

(iii) $y = \dfrac{e^x}{1 + 2e^x} \Rightarrow \dfrac{dy}{dx} = \dfrac{(1 + 2e^x).e^x - e^x.2e^x}{(1 + 2e^x)^2} = \dfrac{e^x}{(1 + 2e^x)^2}$.

Exercise 1.4
Differentiate with respect to the appropriate variable

1 $3x^2$, **2** $7x^2 - \dfrac{3}{x^2}$, **3** $(1 - 3t)^2$, **4** $(2 - x)(x + 4)$, **5** $2\sqrt{x}(1 - 3x + 4x^3)$,

6 $2\sqrt{t}\sin t$, **7** $\sec\theta$, **8** $\cot v$, **9** $e^x\sin x$, **10** $(1 - 2x)\ln x$, **11** $\dfrac{1 - 2x}{1 + 2x}$,

12 $\dfrac{\sqrt{x}}{1 + \sqrt{x}}$, **13** $\dfrac{3 + 2e^x}{2 - e^x}$, **14** $\dfrac{2 + \ln x}{4 + 2\ln x}$, **15** $x^2\sin x\cos x$, **16** $x(1 - 2x)(1 - 3x)$,

17 $\dfrac{1}{(1 + x)(1 - x)}$, **18** $\dfrac{\sin\theta}{\theta}$, **19** $\dfrac{1 + \sin t}{1 - \sin t}$, **20** $\sec u$, **21** $\dfrac{1}{(2 + x)^2}$.

1.5   Function of a function
If u is a function of x, i.e. $u = f(x)$, and y is a function of u, i.e. $y = F(u)$, then we can write $y = F[f(x)]$ and say that y is a *function of a function* of x.

For example, $2 + 3x^2$ is a function of x and $(2 + 3x^2)^3$ is a function of $2 + 3x^2$. Therefore $(2 + 3x^2)^3$ is a function of a function of x.

Similarly, $3t$ is a function of t and $\sin 3t$ is a function of $3t$. Therefore $\sin 3t$ is a function of a function of t.

Other examples of functions of a function are e^{4x}, $e^{4x} + e^{-4x}$, $\ln\left[(2 + t)^2\right]$, $\tan 3t$, $\sin^3 t$, $\dfrac{1}{2 - \sqrt{x}}$ and $\sec\left(3x - \dfrac{\pi}{4}\right)$.

We now show how to differentiate a function of a function. Consider y, a function of u where u is a function of x, i.e. $y = F(u)$ and $u = f(x)$. This implies that y is a function of x. Let x increase by a small amount δx and let the corresponding increments in u and y be δu and δy respectively. Then we can write $\dfrac{\delta y}{\delta x} = \dfrac{\delta y}{\delta u} \cdot \dfrac{\delta u}{\delta x}$, since each of these terms is a fraction,

$$\Rightarrow \lim_{\delta x \to 0} \frac{\delta y}{\delta x} = \lim_{\delta x \to 0} \left(\frac{\delta y}{\delta u} \cdot \frac{\delta u}{\delta x} \right) = \lim_{\delta x \to 0} \frac{\delta y}{\delta u} \cdot \lim_{\delta x \to 0} \frac{\delta u}{\delta x}.$$

But as $\delta x \to 0$, $\delta u \to 0$

$$\Rightarrow \lim_{\delta x \to 0} \frac{\delta y}{\delta x} = \lim_{\delta u \to 0} \frac{\delta y}{\delta u} \cdot \lim_{\delta x \to 0} \frac{\delta u}{\delta x} \Rightarrow \frac{dy}{dx} = \frac{dy}{du} \cdot \frac{du}{dx}.$$

This is known as the *chain rule* or *function of a function rule*. Although it appears that $\dfrac{dy}{du} \cdot \dfrac{du}{dx}$ may be treated as the product of fractions with the du's cancelling, no such cancellation can actually take place. As was stated earlier the du in $\dfrac{dy}{du}$ $\left(\text{or } \dfrac{du}{dx} \right)$ cannot be separated from the dy (or the dx). Remember $\dfrac{dy}{du}$ is not a fraction, but a notation for the result of the operation of taking the limit of $\dfrac{\delta y}{\delta u}$ as δu tends to zero. Nevertheless, in writing down the chain rule terms one inevitably bears in mind the properties of fractions. Thus, for $y = F(u)$ where $u = f(x), \dfrac{dy}{dx} = \dfrac{dy}{du} \dfrac{du}{dx}$.

The chain rule can be further extended to a function of a function of a function, for example $y = F(u)$, where $u = f(v)$ and $v = g(x)$,

$$\Rightarrow \frac{dy}{dx} = \frac{dy}{du} \cdot \frac{du}{dv} \cdot \frac{dv}{dx}.$$

An example of the latter is $y = \sin^3 3x$; $3x$ is a function of x, $\sin 3x$ is a function of $3x$ and $\sin^3 3x$ is a function of $\sin 3x$.

When first differentiating functions of a function it may be found helpful to introduce the extra variables but with practice this should soon become unnecessary.

Example 5 Find $\dfrac{dy}{dx}$ when $y = (2 + 3x^2)^4$.

Let $u = (2 + 3x^2)$ so that $y = u^4$.

$$u = 2 + 3x^2 \Rightarrow \frac{du}{dx} = 6x.$$

$$y = u^4 \qquad \Rightarrow \frac{dy}{du} = 4u^3 = 4(2 + 3x^2)^3.$$

$$\frac{dy}{dx} = \frac{dy}{du} \frac{du}{dx} = 4(2 + 3x^2)^3 \cdot 6x = 24x(2 + 3x^2)^3.$$

It is possible to generalise derivatives of this kind by considering $y = u^n$, where u is a function of x.

$$y = u^n \Rightarrow \frac{dy}{du} = nu^{n-1}$$

$$\Rightarrow \frac{dy}{dx} = \frac{dy}{du}\frac{du}{dx} = nu^{n-1}\frac{du}{dx}.$$

In fact, $y = [f(x)]^n \Rightarrow \frac{dy}{dx} = n[f(x)]^{n-1}. f'(x)$, where $f'(x)$ denotes the derivative of $f(x)$ with respect to x.

Example 6

(i) $y = (2x^3 - x)^4 \Rightarrow \dfrac{dy}{dx} = 4(2x^3 - x)^3 . (2.3x^2 - 1)$

$$= 4(2x^3 - x)^3 . (6x^2 - 1),$$

(ii) $y = \sin^3 x = (\sin x)^3 \Rightarrow \dfrac{dy}{dx} = 3(\sin x)^2 . \cos x$

$$= 3\sin^2 x \cos x,$$

(iii) $y = \left(\dfrac{1 + x}{1 - x}\right)^7 \Rightarrow \dfrac{dy}{dx} = 7\left(\dfrac{1 + x}{1 - x}\right)^6 . \dfrac{(1 - x)1 - (1 + x)(-1)}{(1 - x)^2}$

$$= 7\left(\frac{1 + x}{1 - x}\right)^6 . \frac{2}{(1 - x)^2} = \frac{14(1 + x)^6}{(1 - x)^8}.$$

1.6 Derivatives of the trigonometric functions

We have already stated the results

(i) $y = \sin x \Rightarrow \dfrac{dy}{dx} = \cos x$, (ii) $y = \cos x \Rightarrow \dfrac{dy}{dx} = -\sin x$.

We now find the derivatives of $\sin ax$, $\cos ax$, $\tan ax$, where a is a constant, and powers of these functions.

Consider $y = \sin ax$.

$$u = ax \quad \Rightarrow \frac{du}{dx} = a,$$

$$y = \sin u \Rightarrow \frac{dy}{du} = \cos u = \cos ax,$$

$$\Rightarrow \frac{dy}{dx} = \frac{dy}{du}.\frac{du}{dx} = \cos ax . a = a \cos ax$$

$$\Rightarrow \frac{d}{dx}(\sin ax) = a \cos ax.$$

Similarly, it can be shown that

$$\frac{d}{dx}(\cos ax) = -a \sin ax, \qquad \frac{d}{dx}(\tan ax) = a \sec^2 ax.$$

These results can be generalised further to

(i) $\dfrac{d}{dx} \sin f(x) = \cos f(x).f'(x)$,

(ii) $\dfrac{d}{dx} \cos f(x) = -\sin f(x).f'(x)$,

(iii) $\dfrac{d}{dx} \tan f(x) = \sec^2 f(x).f'(x)$,

where $f'(x)$ denotes the derivative of $f(x)$ with respect to x.

Example 7

(i) $y = \sin(3x^2) \Rightarrow \dfrac{dy}{dx} = \cos(3x^2).6x = 6x \cos(3x^2)$,

(ii) $y = \cos(2x + \pi/4) \Rightarrow \dfrac{dy}{dx} = -\sin(2x + \pi/4).2 = -2 \sin(2x + \pi/4)$,

(iii) $y = \tan(1 - 5x) \Rightarrow \dfrac{dy}{dx} = \sec^2(1 - 5x).(-5) = -5 \sec^2(1 - 5x)$.

Powers of trigonometric functions can be differentiated by using the above in conjunction with the earlier result that

$$\frac{d}{dx}[f(x)]^n = n[f(x)]^{n-1}.f'(x).$$

Example 8

(i) $y = \sin^4 3x = (\sin 3x)^4$

$$\Rightarrow \frac{dy}{dx} = 4(\sin 3x)^3.(3 \cos 3x) = 12 \sin^3 3x \cos 3x,$$

(ii) $y = \sec 2x = (\cos 2x)^{-1}$

$$\Rightarrow \frac{dy}{dx} = (-1)(\cos 2x)^{-2}.(-2 \sin 2x) = \frac{2 \sin 2x}{\cos^2 2x} = 2 \tan 2x \sec 2x.$$

Similarly, in conjunction with the product or quotient rule:

(iii) $y = \sin^4 3x \cos 4x$

$$\Rightarrow \frac{dy}{dx} = (4 \sin^3 3x.3 \cos 3x)\cos 4x + \sin^4 3x(-4 \sin 4x)$$

$$= 12 \sin^3 3x.\cos 3x.\cos 4x - 4 \sin^4 3x.\sin 4x,$$

(iv) $y = \dfrac{1 + \tan 2t}{1 - \tan 2t}$

$$\Rightarrow \frac{dy}{dt} = \frac{(1 - \tan 2t)2 \sec^2 2t - (1 + \tan 2t)(-2 \sec^2 2t)}{(1 - \tan 2t)^2}$$

$$= \frac{4 \sec^2 2t}{(1 - \tan 2t)^2}.$$

1.7 Logarithm and exponential functions

Differentiation of the logarithm and exponential functions can likewise be extended to cases such as

$$\frac{d}{dx}[\ln f(x)] = \frac{f'(x)}{f(x)}, \quad \frac{d}{dx}[e^{f(x)}] = e^{f(x)}.f'(x).$$

Example 9

(i) $y = e^{4x} \Rightarrow \dfrac{dy}{dx} = e^{4x}.4 = 4e^{4x}$,

(ii) $y = 2e^{\sin 3t} \Rightarrow \dfrac{dy}{dt} = 2e^{\sin 3t}.3 \cos 3t = 6 \cos 3t\, e^{\sin 3t}$,

(iii) $y = \ln(3 + 4x) \Rightarrow \dfrac{dy}{dx} = \dfrac{4}{3 + 4x}$,

(iv) $y = \ln(1 - \cos^3 x) \Rightarrow \dfrac{dy}{dx} = \dfrac{3 \cos^2 x \sin x}{1 - \cos^3 x}$,

(v) $y = e^{2t} \cos 5t \Rightarrow \dfrac{dy}{dt} = 2e^{2t} \cos 5t + e^{2t}(-5 \sin 5t)$

$$= e^{2t}(2 \cos 5t - 5 \sin 5t).$$

1.8 Summary

A more extended list of derivatives which the student should learn and be able to apply with confidence is given below.

y	$\dfrac{dy}{dx}$
$[f(x)]^n$	$n[f(x)]^{n-1}f'(x)$
$\sin f(x)$	$f'(x) \cos f(x)$
$\cos f(x)$	$-f'(x) \sin f(x)$
$\tan f(x)$	$f'(x) \sec^2 f(x)$
$e^{f(x)}$	$f'(x)e^{f(x)}$
$\ln f(x)$	$\dfrac{f'(x)}{f(x)}$

This list, together with the sum, product, and quotient rules, should enable differentiation of most of the elementary functions to be carried out with ease.

Exercise 1.8

Differentiate with respect to the appropriate variable. Try and simplify your results where possible.

1 $(3x + 2)^4$, **2** $(x - 1)(x + 2)\sqrt{x}$, **3** $\dfrac{1}{(2 - 5u)^2}$, **4** $\sqrt[3]{(3 - x)}$, **5** $\dfrac{1}{\sqrt{(3 - 7x)}}$,

6 $t\sqrt{(1 + t)}$, **7** $\sqrt{(3x^2 + 2x - 5)}$, **8** $\dfrac{1}{\sqrt{(3 - 5x - x^2)}}$, **9** $\sqrt{\left(\dfrac{u}{1 - u}\right)}$, **10** $\dfrac{\sqrt{(1 - 2u)}}{u^2}$,

11 $\dfrac{3 + x}{5 - 2x}$, **12** $\dfrac{t(t - 2)}{3t - 1}$, **13** $\sin(\theta/3)$, **14** $\cot 2x$, **15** $\sqrt[3]{(\sin t)}$, **16** $\sin^2 2x$,

17 $\theta^3 \cos \theta$, **18** $\operatorname{cosec} 4x$, **19** $\sin^2 x \cos^3 x$, **20** $(1 + 3 \tan \theta)^4$, **21** $\dfrac{3 + 4 \sin x}{4 + 3 \sin x}$,

22 $\dfrac{\cos^2 \theta}{1 + \cos \theta}$, **23** $e^{2t} \tan 2t$, **24** $\cot(\pi/2 - x)$, **25** e^{5x}, **26** $e^{5t - t^2}$, **27** $e^{\sin \theta}$,

28 $\dfrac{1}{e^{2 \cos 2\theta}}$, **29** $\dfrac{e^{2x}}{x^2}$, **30** $e^{-3x} \cos 2x$, **31** $e^{3 - 2t}$, **32** $(e^x - e^{-x})^2$, **33** $\ln(2x - 1)$,

34 $\ln(1 - u^2)$, **35** $\ln\sqrt{(1 - x)}$, **36** $\dfrac{\ln x}{x}$, **37** $\ln[x(1 - 2x)]$, **38** $\ln\sqrt{(\cos 2x)}$,

39 $e^{2t} \ln 4t$, **40** $\ln\left(\dfrac{\cos 3x}{2 - \sin 3x}\right)$.

2 Further differentiation

2.1 Differentiation of implicit functions

So far we have only been concerned with the differentiation of functions defined in the form $y = f(x)$. Such functions are called *explicit* functions since y is defined entirely (i.e. explicitly) in terms of x. It is not always possible to express the relationship between two variables x and y in this form. Often the equation connecting x and y cannot be rearranged so as to give y entirely in terms of x. For instance the equation $x^2 + \sin xy + y^3 = 3$ defines y as a function of x but it is not possible to solve this equation to obtain y explicitly in terms of x. In such cases y is said to be an *implicit* function of x.

When given an implicit function, it is still possible to obtain an expression for $\dfrac{dy}{dx}$, but instead of $\dfrac{dy}{dx}$ being entirely in terms of x it will be in terms of both x and y.

Consider, for instance, the implicit function defined by $y^4 = 3x^2 + 2y^2 - x^3$. To differentiate this equation with respect to x requires differentiation of powers of y with respect to x. This can be done, using the chain rule for a function of a function, thus:

$$z = y^n \Rightarrow \frac{dz}{dx} = \frac{dz}{dy}\frac{dy}{dx} = ny^{n-1}.\frac{dy}{dx},$$

i.e. to differentiate y^n with respect to x we simply differentiate y^n with respect to y and multiply by $\dfrac{dy}{dx}$. Similarly,

$$\frac{d}{dx}f(y) = \left[\frac{d}{dy}f(y)\right].\frac{dy}{dx}.$$

$$y^4 = 3x^2 + 2y^2 - x^3 \Rightarrow \frac{d}{dx}(y^4) = \frac{d}{dx}(3x^2) + \frac{d}{dx}(2y^2) - \frac{d}{dx}(x^3)$$

and, using the above result, we find

$$4y^3\frac{dy}{dx} = 6x + 4y\frac{dy}{dx} - 3x^2 \Rightarrow \frac{dy}{dx} = \frac{6x - 3x^2}{4y^3 - 4y}.$$

Should the implicit relationship contain product or quotient terms, then it will of course be necessary to observe the rules for differentiating such terms.

Example 1   Find $\dfrac{dy}{dx}$ when $2 \sin 3x + 4x^2 y = x^3 \tan 2y$.

$$\frac{d}{dx}(2 \sin 3x) + \frac{d}{dx}(4x^2 y) = \frac{d}{dx}(x^3 \tan 2y)$$

$$\Rightarrow 6 \cos 3x + 4\left(x^2 . \frac{dy}{dx} + 2x . y\right) = x^3 . 2 \sec^2 2y . \frac{dy}{dx} + 3x^2 \tan 2y$$

$$\Rightarrow \frac{dy}{dx} = \frac{6 \cos 3x + 8xy - 3x^2 \tan 2y}{2x^3 \sec^2 2y - 4x^2}.$$

Exercise 2.1

Find $\dfrac{dy}{dx}$ when x and y are connected by the following equations.

1 $x^2 - y^2 = 4$,   **2** $\dfrac{x^2}{4} + \dfrac{y^2}{9} = 1$,   **3** $x^2 + y^2 - 4x + 6y - 29 = 0$

4 $3x^4 + 4x^2 y^2 - 7y^3 = 0$,   **5** $(x^2 + y^2)^2 = x^3 + y^3$,   **6** $\ln\left(\dfrac{x}{y}\right) = x^2 - y^2$,

7 $3x^2 y - y^2 \sin 2x + \cos(xy) = 0$.

2.2   Higher derivatives

Except when $y[= f(x)]$ is a linear function of x, the derivative will also be a function of x. It can therefore be differentiated with respect to x to give what is known as the *second derivative* of y with respect to x and is denoted by $\dfrac{d^2 y}{dx^2}$.

Further differentiation can usually be carried out leading to the third, fourth, fifth, ..., nth derivatives. These are denoted by $\dfrac{d^3 y}{dx^3}, \dfrac{d^4 y}{dx^4}, \dfrac{d^5 y}{dx^5}, \dots, \dfrac{d^n y}{dx^n}$ respectively.

Useful alternative notations for derivatives of the function defined by $y = f(x)$ include

$$f'(x), f''(x), f'''(x), \dots, f^{(n)}(x)$$

or

$$y'(x), y''(x), y'''(x), \dots, y^{(n)}(x)$$

or

$$y_1(x), y_2(x), y_3(x), \dots, y_n(x).$$

The value of $\dfrac{dy}{dx}$ when $x = 0$ can be written as $\left(\dfrac{dy}{dx}\right)_0 = f'(0) = y'(0) = y_1(0)$, and similarly for higher derivatives.

Example 2   Find the first, second and third derivatives of y with respect to x when (i) $y = x^7$, (ii) $y = \sin 3x$, (iii) $y = \ln(2x)$.

(i) $y = x^7 \Rightarrow \dfrac{dy}{dx} = 7x^6$, $\dfrac{d^2 y}{dx^2} = 7.6.x^5 = 42x^5$, $\dfrac{d^3 y}{dx^3} = 42.5x^4 = 210x^4$,

(ii) $y = \sin 3x \Rightarrow y'(x) = 3 \cos 3x, \quad y''(x) = -9 \sin 3x, \quad y'''(x) = -27 \cos 3x,$

(iii) $y = \ln(2x) \Rightarrow y_1(x) = \dfrac{2}{2x} = \dfrac{1}{x}, \quad y_2(x) = -(x)^{-2} = -\dfrac{1}{x^2},$

$$y_3(x) = -(-2)x^{-3} = \dfrac{2}{x^3}.$$

Example 3   If $y = \sin(\ln x)$, prove that $x^2 \dfrac{d^2 y}{dx^2} + x \dfrac{dy}{dx} + y = 0.$

$y = \sin(\ln x) \Rightarrow \dfrac{dy}{dx} = \cos(\ln x) \cdot \dfrac{1}{x},$

$\Rightarrow \dfrac{d^2 y}{dx^2} = -\sin(\ln x) \cdot \dfrac{1}{x} \cdot \dfrac{1}{x} + \cos(\ln x) \cdot \left(\dfrac{-1}{x^2} \right) = \left(-\dfrac{1}{x^2} \right) [\sin(\ln x) + \cos(\ln x)]$

$\Rightarrow x^2 \dfrac{d^2 y}{dx^2} + x \dfrac{dy}{dx} + y = x^2 \cdot \left(\dfrac{1}{x^2} \right) - [\sin (\ln x) + \cos (\ln x)]$

$$+ x \cdot \cos(\ln x) \dfrac{1}{x} + \sin(\ln x)$$

$$= (-1 + 1)\sin(\ln x) + (-1 + 1)\cos(\ln x) = 0.$$

A better method

Instead of finding the derivatives and substituting their values into the L.H.S. of the equation, we could have actually formed the equation from $y = \sin(\ln x)$ as follows.

$$\dfrac{dy}{dx} = \cos(\ln x) \cdot \dfrac{1}{x} \Rightarrow x \dfrac{dy}{dx} = \cos(\ln x)$$

$$\Rightarrow \dfrac{d}{dx}\left(x \dfrac{dy}{dx} \right) = \dfrac{d}{dx}[\cos(\ln x)]$$

$\Rightarrow x \dfrac{d^2 y}{dx^2} + 1 \cdot \dfrac{dy}{dx} = -\sin(\ln x) \cdot \dfrac{1}{x} = -y \dfrac{1}{x} \quad$ since $\sin(\ln x) = y.$

Multiplying by x $\qquad \Rightarrow x^2 \dfrac{d^2 y}{dx^2} + x \dfrac{dy}{dx} + y = 0.$

Alternatively, $\qquad x \dfrac{dy}{dx} = \cos(\ln x) \Rightarrow x^2 \left(\dfrac{dy}{dx} \right)^2 = \cos^2(\ln x) = 1 - y^2.$

Differentiating w.r. to x $\qquad \Rightarrow x^2 \cdot 2 \dfrac{dy}{dx} \cdot \dfrac{d^2 y}{dx^2} + 2x \left(\dfrac{dy}{dx} \right)^2 = -2y \dfrac{dy}{dx}.$

Hence cancelling $2\dfrac{dy}{dx}$ we obtain the required result.

Most examples of this kind can be worked without explicit calculation of the higher derivatives.

Example 4 If $x^2 + y^2 = 2y$, find $\dfrac{dy}{dx}$ in terms of x and y without first finding y in terms of x. Prove that $\dfrac{d^2y}{dx^2} = \dfrac{1}{(1-y)^3}$.

$$x^2 + y^2 = 2y \Rightarrow \frac{d}{dx}(x^2) + \frac{d}{dx}(y^2) = \frac{d}{dx}(2y)$$

$$\Rightarrow 2x + 2y\frac{dy}{dx} = 2\frac{dy}{dx}$$

$$\Rightarrow \frac{dy}{dx}(1-y) = x \Leftrightarrow \frac{dy}{dx} = \frac{x}{1-y}.$$

Differentiating with respect to x gives

$$\frac{d}{dx}\left[(1-y)\frac{dy}{dx}\right] = \frac{d}{dx}(x)$$

$$\Rightarrow (1-y)\frac{d^2y}{dx^2} + \left(-\frac{dy}{dx}\right)\left(\frac{dy}{dx}\right) = 1$$

$$\Rightarrow (1-y)\frac{d^2y}{dx^2} = 1 + \left(\frac{dy}{dx}\right)^2 = 1 + \frac{x^2}{(1-y)^2} = 1 + \frac{2y - y^2}{(1-y)^2}$$

$$\Rightarrow (1-y)\frac{d^2y}{dx^2} = \frac{(1-y)^2 + 2y - y^2}{(1-y)^2} = \frac{1}{(1-y)^2}$$

$$\Rightarrow \frac{d^2y}{dx^2} = \frac{1}{(1-y)^3}.$$

2.3 Parametric equations

It is quite common for a relationship between x and y to be defined by using a third variable, say t. For instance an alternative form for expressing the relationship $y^2 = 4x$ would be to state the two equations $y = 2t, x = t^2$ since, whatever the value of t, $y^2 = 4x$ as can easily be verified. The equations $y = 2t, x = t^2$ are said to be the *parametric equations* of the curve $y^2 = 4x$.

Other examples of parametric equations are

(i) $x = 3\cos\theta, y = 4\sin\theta \Rightarrow x^2/9 + y^2/16 = 1,$

(ii) $x = 8\cos^3 t, y = 8\sin^3 t \Rightarrow x^{2/3} + y^{2/3} = 4.$

Parametric equations are often used to facilitate working, particularly in coordinate geometry. In the examples given above it is easy to eliminate the third variable and establish an implicit relationship between x and y, but this is by no means always the case. Even so, it is often preferable to work with parametric equations rather than the implicit equation.

By use of the chain rule, we can obtain the derivatives of functions when expressed in parametric form.

Example 5 If $y = 2t$ and $x = t^2$, find $\dfrac{dy}{dx}$ in terms of t.

$$y = 2t \Rightarrow \frac{dy}{dt} = 2, \quad x = t^2 \Rightarrow \frac{dx}{dt} = 2t.$$

Then
$$\frac{dy}{dt} = \frac{dy}{dx} \cdot \frac{dx}{dt} \Rightarrow 2 = \frac{dy}{dx} \cdot 2t \Rightarrow \frac{dy}{dx} = \frac{1}{t}.$$

Example 6 If $x = a(\theta + \sin \theta)$, $y = a(1 - \cos \theta)$, where a is a constant, show that $\dfrac{dy}{dx} = \tan\left(\dfrac{\theta}{2}\right)$ and $\dfrac{d^2y}{dx^2} = \dfrac{1}{4a \cos^4(\theta/2)}$.

$$x = a(\theta + \sin \theta) \Rightarrow \frac{dx}{d\theta} = a(1 + \cos \theta),$$

$$y = a(1 - \cos \theta) \Rightarrow \frac{dy}{d\theta} = a \sin \theta.$$

$$\frac{dy}{d\theta} = \frac{dy}{dx} \frac{dx}{d\theta} \Rightarrow a \sin \theta = \frac{dy}{dx} \cdot a(1 + \cos \theta)$$

$$\Rightarrow \frac{dy}{dx} = \frac{a \sin \theta}{a(1 + \cos \theta)} = \frac{2 \sin(\theta/2) \cos(\theta/2)}{1 + 2 \cos^2(\theta/2) - 1} = \tan(\theta/2),$$

since $\sin \theta = 2 \sin(\theta/2) \cos(\theta/2)$ and $\cos \theta = 2 \cos^2(\theta/2) - 1$.

For the second derivative, $\dfrac{d^2y}{dx^2} = \dfrac{d}{dx}\left(\dfrac{dy}{dx}\right) = \dfrac{d}{dx}[\tan(\theta/2)] = \dfrac{1}{2} \sec^2(\theta/2)\dfrac{d\theta}{dx}$

since, as we showed earlier, $\dfrac{d}{dx} \cdot f(\theta) = \left[\dfrac{d}{d\theta}f(\theta)\right] \cdot \dfrac{d\theta}{dx}$.

Now by the chain rule, $\dfrac{dx}{d\theta} \cdot \dfrac{d\theta}{dx} = 1 \Rightarrow \dfrac{d\theta}{dx} = 1 \bigg/ \dfrac{dx}{d\theta}$

$$\Rightarrow \frac{d\theta}{dx} = \frac{1}{a(1 + \cos \theta)}$$

$$\Rightarrow \frac{d^2y}{dx^2} = \frac{1}{2} \sec^2(\theta/2) \cdot \frac{1}{a(1 + \cos \theta)}$$

$$= \frac{1}{2 \cos^2(\theta/2)} \cdot \frac{1}{a \cdot 2 \cos^2(\theta/2)} = \frac{1}{4a \cos^4(\theta/2)}.$$

Second derivatives are so frequently required that it is advantageous to establish a general result. Thus, if $x = x(t)$, $y = y(t)$, then $\dfrac{dy}{dx} = \dfrac{dy}{dt} \cdot \dfrac{dt}{dx} = \dfrac{\dot{y}}{\dot{x}}$ where the dots denote derivatives w.r. to t.

Hence,
$$\frac{d^2y}{dx^2} = \frac{d}{dx}\left(\frac{dy}{dx}\right) = \frac{dt}{dx} \cdot \frac{d}{dt}\left(\frac{\dot{y}}{\dot{x}}\right)$$

$$\Rightarrow \frac{d^2y}{dx^2} = \frac{1}{\dot{x}} \cdot \frac{\dot{x}\cdot\ddot{y} - \dot{y}\cdot\ddot{x}}{\dot{x}^2} = \frac{\dot{x}\ddot{y} - \dot{y}\ddot{x}}{\dot{x}^3}.$$

2.4 The exponential function

The function exp x is called the *exponential function* which we define as that function whose derivative is the same function.

$$y = \exp x \Rightarrow \frac{dy}{dx} = \exp x.$$

From other considerations it can be shown that exp x can be written as e^x where e is a constant approximately equal to 2·71828 and also that

$$e^x = 1 + \frac{x}{1!} + \frac{x^2}{2!} + \frac{x^3}{3!} + \frac{x^4}{4!} + \ldots + \frac{x^n}{n!} + \ldots.$$

It has already been stated that for the more generalised form

$$y = e^{f(x)} \Rightarrow \frac{dy}{dx} = e^{f(x)} \cdot f'(x).$$

Example 7 Given that $y = e^{3\sqrt{(1-x)}}$, prove that $4(1 - x)\dfrac{d^2y}{dx^2} - 2\dfrac{dy}{dx} - 9y = 0$.

$$y = e^{3\sqrt{(1-x)}} \Rightarrow \frac{dy}{dx} = e^{3\sqrt{(1-x)}} \cdot \left(-\frac{3}{2}\right)(1 - x)^{-1/2}.$$

Rearranging,

$$2(1 - x)^{1/2}\frac{dy}{dx} = -3e^{3\sqrt{(1-x)}}.$$

Differentiation again w.r. to x

$$\Rightarrow 2(1 - x)^{1/2}\frac{d^2y}{dx^2} + \frac{dy}{dx} \cdot 2 \cdot \left(\frac{1}{2}\right)(1 - x)^{-1/2}(-1)$$

$$= -3e^{3\sqrt{(1-x)}} \cdot 3\left(-\frac{1}{2}\right)(1 - x)^{-1/2}$$

and multiplying through by $2(1 - x)^{1/2}$

$$\Rightarrow 4(1-x)\frac{d^2y}{dx^2} - 2\frac{dy}{dx} = 9e^{3\sqrt{(1-x)}} = 9y$$

$$\Rightarrow 4(1-x)\frac{d^2y}{dx^2} - 2\frac{dy}{dx} - 9y = 0.$$

A better method

After establishing the result for the first derivative a better method would have been to proceed as follows:

$$2(1-x)^{1/2}\frac{dy}{dx} = -3e^{3\sqrt{(1-x)}} = -3y \Rightarrow 4(1-x)\left(\frac{dy}{dx}\right)^2 = 9y^2.$$

Differentiation w.r. to x

$$\Rightarrow 4(1-x).2\left(\frac{dy}{dx}\right)\left(\frac{d^2y}{dx^2}\right) + 4(-1)\left(\frac{dy}{dx}\right)^2 = 18y\frac{dy}{dx}$$

and dividing this equation by $2\dfrac{dy}{dx}$ gives

$$4(1-x)\frac{d^2y}{dx^2} - 2\frac{dy}{dx} - 9y = 0.$$

2.5 The logarithm function

If $y = e^x$, then by definition x is said to be the *logarithm* of y to the base e, written as $x = \log_e y$ or $\ln y$.

Alternatively, relabelling $y = \ln x$ would require $x = e^y$. From this we can verify the result quoted earlier that $y = \ln x \Rightarrow \dfrac{dy}{dx} = \dfrac{1}{x}$.

Now
$$y = \ln x \Rightarrow x = e^y$$

and
$$x = e^y \Rightarrow \frac{d}{dx}(x) = \frac{d}{dx}(e^y)$$

$$\Rightarrow 1 = e^y\frac{dy}{dx} \Rightarrow \frac{dy}{dx} = \frac{1}{x}.$$

More generally,
$$y = \ln f(x) \Rightarrow \frac{dy}{dx} = \frac{f'(x)}{f(x)}.$$

2.6 Uses of logarithmic differentiation

We have seen that for *the* exponential function $y = e^x$, $\dfrac{dy}{dx} = e^x$. If $y = a^x$, where a is any constant other than e, then the function $y = a^x$ is called *an* exponential function and its derivative is not quite of the same form as that for *the* exponential function.

To obtain the derivative of a^x we proceed as follows.

$y = a^x \Leftrightarrow \ln y = \ln a^x = x \ln a$, by the laws of logarithms,

$$\Rightarrow \frac{d}{dx}(\ln y) = \frac{d}{dx}(x \ln a)$$

$$\Rightarrow \frac{1}{y}\frac{dy}{dx} = 1 . \ln a$$

$$\Rightarrow \frac{dy}{dx} = y \ln a = a^x \ln a.$$

This procedure is normal practice for the derivative of any function (other than *the* exponential function) where the variable occurs in the index.

Example 8 $y = x^x \Rightarrow \ln y = \ln x^x = x \ln x$

$$\Rightarrow \frac{d}{dx}(\ln y) = \frac{d}{dx}(x \ln x)$$

$$\Rightarrow \frac{1}{y}\frac{dy}{dx} = x . \frac{1}{x} + 1 . \ln x$$

$$\Rightarrow \frac{dy}{dx} = y(1 + \ln x) = x^x(1 + \ln x).$$

Logarithmic differentiation is also very effective when considering the derivative of a function consisting of the product of a number of terms. Consider for instance the function

$y = \dfrac{u_1 . u_2 . u_3 . \ \ldots \ u_m}{v_1 . v_2 . v_3 . \ \ldots \ v_n}$, where u_1, u_2, u_3, $\ldots$, u_m, v_1, v_2, v_3, $\ldots$, v_n are all functions of x.

Taking logarithms of both sides and using the properties of logarithms we obtain

$$\ln y = (\ln u_1 + \ln u_2 + \ldots + \ln u_m) - (\ln v_1 + \ln v_2 + \ldots + \ln v_n)$$

$$\Rightarrow \frac{1}{y}\frac{dy}{dx} = \left(\frac{1}{u_1}\frac{du_1}{dx} + \frac{1}{u_2}\frac{du_2}{dx} + \ldots + \frac{1}{u_m}\frac{du_m}{dx}\right)$$

$$- \left(\frac{1}{v_1}\frac{dv_1}{dx} + \frac{1}{v_2}\frac{dv_2}{dx} + \ldots + \frac{1}{v_n}\frac{dv_n}{dx}\right),$$

from which $\dfrac{dy}{dx}$ can easily be obtained.

Example 9   Find $\dfrac{dy}{dx}$ when $y = \sqrt{\left(\dfrac{1 - x^2}{1 + x^2}\right)}$.

$$y = \sqrt{\left(\frac{1 - x^2}{1 + x^2}\right)} \Rightarrow \ln y = \frac{1}{2} \ln(1 - x^2) - \frac{1}{2} \ln(1 + x^2)$$

$$\Rightarrow \frac{1}{y} \frac{dy}{dx} = \frac{1}{2} \cdot \frac{-2x}{1 - x^2} - \frac{1}{2} \cdot \frac{2x}{1 + x^2} = -x \left(\frac{1}{1 - x^2} + \frac{1}{1 + x^2}\right)$$

$$= \frac{-2x}{(1 - x^2)(1 + x^2)}$$

$$\Rightarrow \frac{dy}{dx} = \frac{-2xy}{(1 - x^2)(1 + x^2)}, \quad \text{or, substituting for } y,$$

$$\frac{dy}{dx} = \frac{-2x}{\sqrt{[(1 - x^2)(1 + x^2)^3]}}.$$

Example 10 If $e^{2y} = \dfrac{(2 - x)^{1/2} \cos 3x}{(1 + x)^x}$, find the value of $\dfrac{dy}{dx}$ when $x = 0$.

Taking logarithms,

$$\ln e^{2y} = 2y = \frac{1}{2} \ln(2 - x) + \ln \cos 3x - x \ln(1 + x)$$

$$\Rightarrow 2 \frac{dy}{dx} = \frac{1}{2} \cdot \frac{-1}{(2 - x)} + \frac{-3 \sin 3x}{\cos 3x} - x \cdot \frac{1}{1 + x} - 1 \cdot \ln(1 + x)$$

$$\Rightarrow 2 \left(\frac{dy}{dx}\right)_0 = \frac{1}{2}\left(-\frac{1}{2}\right) - 0 - 0 - 0 = -\frac{1}{4} \Rightarrow \left(\frac{dy}{dx}\right)_0 = -\frac{1}{8}.$$

In differentiating logarithms it should be noted that all logarithms should be taken to the base e. If the base is anything other than e, then it is necessary to use the change of base formula,

$$\log_a x = \frac{\log_b x}{\log_b a},$$

to change the bases to e before differentiating.

Example 11 Find $\dfrac{dy}{dx}$ when $y = \log_{10} x$. [Note $\log_{10} x$ is often denoted by lg x.]

$$y = \log_{10} x = \frac{\log_e x}{\log_e 10} = \left(\frac{1}{\ln 10}\right) \cdot \ln x$$

$$\Rightarrow \frac{dy}{dx} = \frac{1}{\ln 10} \cdot \frac{1}{x}.$$

2.7 Inverse trigonometric functions

The function $y = \sin x$ is a many–one mapping as shown by its graph in Fig. 2.1. Consequently, it is only possible to speak of its inverse relation as being a

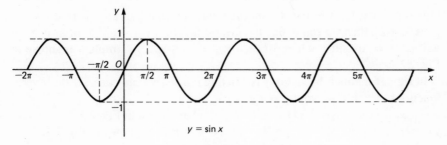

$y = \sin x$

Fig. 2.1

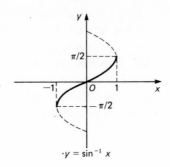

$\cdot y = \sin^{-1} x$

Fig. 2.2

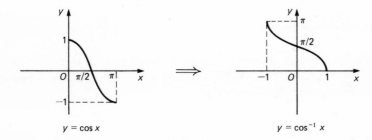

$y = \cos x$ $y = \cos^{-1} x$

Fig. 2.3

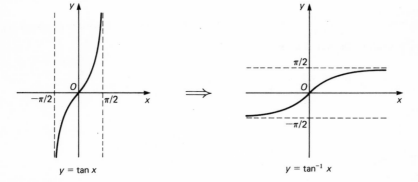

$y = \tan x$ $y = \tan^{-1} x$

Fig. 2.4

function if there is a restriction on the range. Thus, if the range is restricted to $[-\pi/2, \pi/2]$, then we can define the inverse function $y = \sin^{-1} x$, or as is often written, $y = \text{arc sin } x$, where $y \in \mathbb{R}$, $-\pi/2 \leqslant y \leqslant \pi/2$. Its graph is as shown in Fig. 2.2.

In similar manner, by suitably restricting ranges, we can consider the inverse functions of $y = \cos x$ and $y = \tan x$.

$y = \cos x \Rightarrow y = \cos^{-1} x$ ($y \in \mathbb{R}$, $0 \leqslant y \leqslant \pi$) as shown in Fig. 2.3.

$y = \tan x \Rightarrow y = \tan^{-1} x$ ($y \in \mathbb{R}$, $-\pi/2 < y < \pi/2$) as shown in Fig. 2.4.

The restriction on the range of the inverse functions leads to what are known as the *principal values* of the functions. Thus:

$y = \sin^{-1} x \Rightarrow$ for given x, y has a principal value in $[-\pi/2, \pi/2]$

$y = \cos^{-1} x \Rightarrow$ for given x, y has a principal value in $[0, \pi]$

$y = \tan^{-1} x \Rightarrow$ for given x, y has a principal value in $(-\pi/2, \pi/2)$.

Principal values are extremely important in differential and integral calculus and it must be clearly understood that when dealing with the inverse trigonometric functions the principal values are always taken.

The derivatives of the inverse trigonometric functions can be found as follows.

$$y = \sin^{-1} x \Rightarrow \sin y = x$$

$$\Rightarrow \cos y \frac{dy}{dx} = 1 \Rightarrow \frac{dy}{dx} = \frac{1}{\cos y}.$$

To obtain the value in terms of x,

$$\frac{dy}{dx} = \frac{1}{\sqrt{(\cos^2 y)}}$$

$$\Rightarrow \frac{dy}{dx} = \frac{1}{\sqrt{(1 - \sin^2 y)}} = \frac{1}{\sqrt{(1 - x^2)}},$$

the positive sign being taken, since, within the range of the function, the gradient of the tangent is always positive, as shown in Fig. 2.2.

Hence,
$$\frac{d}{dx}(\sin^{-1} x) = \frac{1}{\sqrt{(1 - x^2)}}.$$

In similar manner it can be shown that

$$\frac{d}{dx}(\cos^{-1} x) = \frac{-1}{\sqrt{(1 - x^2)}}, \qquad \frac{d}{dx}(\tan^{-1} x) = \frac{1}{1 + x^2}.$$

More generally

$$\frac{d}{dx}[\sin^{-1} f(x)] = \frac{f'(x)}{\sqrt{\{1 - [f(x)]^2\}}},$$

$$\frac{d}{dx}[\cos^{-1} f(x)] = \frac{-f'(x)}{\sqrt{\{1 - [f(x)]^2\}}},$$

$$\frac{d}{dx}[\tan^{-1} f(x)] = \frac{f'(x)}{1 + [f(x)]^2}.$$

Students should add these to their list of standard derivatives.

Example 12

(i) $y = \sin^{-1}\left(\dfrac{x}{a}\right) \Rightarrow \dfrac{dy}{dx} = \dfrac{1/a}{\sqrt{[1 - (x/a)^2]}} = \dfrac{1}{\sqrt{(a^2 - x^2)}}, \quad a > 0,$

(ii) $y = \tan^{-1}\left(\dfrac{x}{a}\right) \Rightarrow \dfrac{dy}{dx} = \dfrac{1/a}{1 + (x/a)^2} = \dfrac{a}{a^2 + x^2}, \quad a > 0,$

(iii) $y = \sin^{-1}(xe^x) \Rightarrow \dfrac{dy}{dx} = \dfrac{1 \cdot e^x + xe^x}{\sqrt{[1 - (xe^x)^2]}} = \dfrac{e^x(1 + x)}{\sqrt{[1 - x^2 e^{2x}]}},$

(iv) $y = \tan^{-1}\left(\dfrac{x}{1 - x}\right) \Rightarrow \dfrac{dy}{dx} = \dfrac{[(1 - x) \cdot 1 - x(-1)]/(1 - x)^2}{1 + [x/(1 - x)]^2}$

$$= \frac{1}{1 - 2x + 2x^2}.$$

Exercise 2.7

1   Given that $2ye^{3x} + \dfrac{1}{x^2} \sin 2x = 0$, find $\dfrac{dy}{dx}$.

2   Show that $y = x^2 \sin 2x$ satisfies the equation

$$\frac{d^2y}{dx^2} + 4y = \frac{4}{x}\frac{dy}{dx} - 6 \sin 2x.$$

3   If $y = \sqrt{(5x^2 + 3)}$, show that $y\dfrac{d^2y}{dx^2} + \left(\dfrac{dy}{dx}\right)^2 = 5.$

4   If $y = xe^{-x}$, prove that $\dfrac{d^2y}{dx^2} + 2\dfrac{dy}{dx} + y = 0$. Hence find the value of $\dfrac{d^6y}{dx^6}$ when $x = 0$.

5   Find $\dfrac{dy}{dx}$ in its simplest form in terms of t when $x = e^t \cos t, \, y = e^t \sin t$.

6   If $x = \dfrac{1 + t}{1 - 2t}$ and $y = \dfrac{1 + 2t}{1 - t}$, find the value of $\dfrac{dy}{dx}$ when $t = 0$.

7   If $x = a(\cos \theta + \theta \sin \theta), \, y = a(\sin \theta - \theta \cos \theta)$, show that

(i) $x^2 + y^2 = a^2(1 + \theta^2)$, (ii) $\dfrac{dy}{dx} = \tan \theta$, (iii) $\dfrac{d^2y}{dx^2} = \dfrac{1}{a\theta \cos^3 \theta}.$

8   If $y = a^x$, where a is a constant, prove that

(i) $\dfrac{dy}{dx} = y \ln a$, (ii) $y\dfrac{d^2y}{dx^2} = \left(\dfrac{dy}{dx}\right)^2$, (iii) $\dfrac{d^ny}{dx^n} = y(\ln a)^n.$

9   If $y = \ln \sin u$ and $x = \tan u$, prove that $\dfrac{d^2y}{dx^2} = 2\left(\dfrac{dy}{dx}\right)^2 - \dfrac{3}{x}\dfrac{dy}{dx}.$

10   If $\dfrac{dy}{dx} = x + \dfrac{1}{y}$, find the value of $\dfrac{d^2x}{dy^2}$ in terms of x and y only and no other derivatives.

$\left(\text{Hint, use } \dfrac{dy}{dx} = 1 \middle/ \dfrac{dx}{dy}.\right)$

11 Given that $y^2 = \dfrac{(2 + x)^4 \cdot e^{3x^2} \cdot \cos 4x}{\sqrt{(1 - x^2)}}$, find the value of $\dfrac{dy}{dx}$ when $x = 0$.

12 If $y = \sin 2x$, prove that $\dfrac{d^2y}{dx^2} = 4 \sin(2x + \pi)$. Hence show that

$$\frac{d^{2n}y}{dx^{2n}} = 4^n \sin(2x + n\pi).$$

13 Given that $y = (p + x)\cos x$, where p is a constant, find $\dfrac{d^2y}{dx^2} + y$ and show that it is independent of p.

14 Differentiate with respect to the appropriate variable and simplify:

(i) $\sin^{-1}(x^2)$, (ii) $\tan^{-1}(1 - t)$, (iii) $\cos^{-1}\left(\dfrac{1}{\sqrt{x}}\right)$, (iv) arc tan(cot θ),

(v) arc $\sin\left(\dfrac{1}{1 + x}\right)$, (vi) $\sin^{-1}(e^x \sin x)$.

15 Differentiate arc $\sin(1 - x^2)$, where $0 < x < \sqrt{2}$, and simplify your result. (L)

16 If $y = x$ arc tan x, show that

(i) $x(1 + x^2)\dfrac{dy}{dx} = x^2 + (1 + x^2)y$, (ii) $(1 + x^2)\dfrac{d^2y}{dx^2} + 2x\dfrac{dy}{dx} - 2y = 2$. (L)

17 If $y =$ arc tan x, prove that

$$\frac{d^2y}{dx^2} + 2x\left(\frac{dy}{dx}\right)^2 = 0$$

and deduce that

$$\frac{d^3y}{dx^3} - 8x^2\left(\frac{dy}{dx}\right)^3 + 2\left(\frac{dy}{dx}\right)^2 = 0. \tag{L}$$

18 If $y = (\sin^{-1} x)^2$, prove that

$$(1 - x^2)\left(\frac{dy}{dx}\right)^2 = 4y$$

and deduce that

$$(1 - x^2)\frac{d^2y}{dx^2} - x\frac{dy}{dx} - 2 = 0.$$

3 Applications of differentiation

3.1 Introduction

In chapter 1 we saw that, for a function defined by $y = f(x)$, the derivative $\dfrac{dy}{dx}$ is a measure of (i) the gradient of the tangent to the curve $y = f(x)$ at any point (x, y) on the curve, and (ii) the exact rate of change of y with respect to x. This leads immediately to two important applications of differentiation.

3.2 Equations of tangents and normals

The equation of a straight line of gradient m passing through the point (x_1, y_1) is given by $y - y_1 = m(x - x_1)$. Consequently, when given a point (x_1, y_1) on a curve $y = f(x)$, the gradient m of the tangent at that point is found by substituting $x = x_1$, $y = y_1$ in the value of $\dfrac{dy}{dx}$. Hence, knowing m and (x_1, y_1), the equation of the tangent can be obtained from $y - y_1 = m(x - x_1)$.

Example 1   Find the equation of the tangent to the curve $y = 7x^3 - 3x - 2$ at the point $(1, 2)$. Find also the equation of the normal to the curve at this point.

$$y = 7x^3 - 3x^2 - 2 \Rightarrow \frac{dy}{dx} = 21x^2 - 6x$$

$\Rightarrow$ the gradient of the tangent to the curve at the point $(1, 2)$ is $21.1 - 6.1 = 15$
$\Rightarrow$ equation of the tangent to the curve at $(1, 2)$ is

$$y - 2 = 15(x - 1) \Leftrightarrow y = 15x - 13.$$

Two lines are perpendicular when the product of their gradients m_1 and m_2 is -1. Hence, if m_2 is the gradient of the normal to the curve at $(1, 2)$, then, since the gradient, m_1, of the tangent at that point is 15,

$$15 . m_2 = -1 \Leftrightarrow m_2 = -\frac{1}{15}$$

$\Rightarrow$ equation of the normal to the curve at $(1, 2)$ is

$$y - 2 = -\frac{1}{15}(x - 1) \Leftrightarrow 15y + x = 31.$$

The same procedure applies if the curve is given in parametric form, the only difference being the extra work involved in the calculation of the differential coefficient.

Example 2 The parametric equations of a curve are $x = \cos 2t$, $y = 4 \sin t$. Sketch the curve for $0 \leqslant t \leqslant \pi/2$.

Show that $\dfrac{dy}{dx} = -\operatorname{cosec} t$ and find the equation of the tangent to the curve at the point A ($\cos 2T$, $4 \sin T$).

The tangent at A crosses the x-axis at the point M, and the normal at A crosses the x-axis at the point N. If the area of the triangle AMN is $12 \sin T$, find the value of T between 0 and $\pi/2$.

When $t = 0$, $x = 1$, $y = 0$.
When $t = \pi/4$, $x = 0$, $y = 2\sqrt{2}$.
When $t = \pi/2$, $x = -1$, $y = 4$.

As t increases from 0 to $\pi/2$, x decreases from 1 to -1 and y increases from 0 to 4. The curve is as shown in Fig. 3.1.

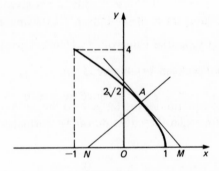

Fig. 3.1

$$x = \cos 2t \Rightarrow \frac{dx}{dt} = -2 \sin 2t, \qquad y = 4 \sin t \Rightarrow \frac{dy}{dt} = 4 \cos t$$

$$\Rightarrow \frac{dy}{dx} = \frac{dy}{dt} \bigg/ \frac{dx}{dt} = 4 \cos t \cdot \frac{1}{-2 \sin 2t}$$

$$= \frac{-2 \cos t}{2 \sin t \cos t}, \qquad \text{since } \sin 2t = 2 \sin t \cos t,$$

$$= -\frac{1}{\sin t} = -\operatorname{cosec} t$$

$\Rightarrow$ at the point $(\cos 2T, 4 \sin T)$, $t = T$ and the gradient of the tangent is $-\operatorname{cosec} T$
$\Rightarrow$ equation of the tangent at $(\cos 2T, 4 \sin T)$ is

$$y - 4 \sin T = -\operatorname{cosec} T(x - \cos 2T)$$

$$\Rightarrow y \sin T + x = 4 \sin^2 T + \cos 2T = 4 \sin^2 T + 1 - 2 \sin^2 T$$

$$\Rightarrow y \sin T + x = 2 \sin^2 T + 1.$$

At M, $y = 0 \Rightarrow x = 2 \sin^2 T + 1 \Rightarrow OM = 2 \sin^2 T + 1.$

If m is the gradient of the normal at A, $m(-\operatorname{cosec} T) = -1 \Rightarrow m = \sin T$
$\Rightarrow$ equation of the normal at A is

$$y - 4 \sin T = \sin T(x - \cos 2T).$$

At N, $y = 0 \Rightarrow x = \cos 2T - 4 \Rightarrow ON = |\cos 2T - 4|,$

$$\Rightarrow MN = OM + ON = 2 \sin^2 T + 1 + 4 - \cos 2T$$

$$= 5 + 2 \sin^2 T - \cos 2T$$

$$= 5 + 2 \sin^2 T - (1 - 2 \sin^2 T)$$

$$= 4(1 + \sin^2 T)$$

$$\Rightarrow \text{area } \triangle AMN = \tfrac{1}{2} \text{ base} \times \text{height}$$

$$= \tfrac{1}{2}MN \times (y\text{-coordinate of } A)$$

$$= \tfrac{1}{2}.4(1 + \sin^2 T).4 \sin T = 8 \sin T(1 + \sin^2 T).$$

But this is given to be $12 \sin T$

$$\Rightarrow 12 \sin T = 8 \sin T(1 + \sin^2 T)$$

$$\Rightarrow 12 = 8 + 8 \sin^2 T, \text{ since } \sin T \neq 0,$$

$$\Rightarrow \sin T = 1/\sqrt{2} \Rightarrow T = \pi/4, \text{ since } 0 < T < \pi/2.$$

Exercise 3.2

1 If $x = 4t - t^2$ and $y = 3 + t^3$, show that, when $t = 1$, $\dfrac{dy}{dx} = \dfrac{3}{2}$. Hence, or otherwise, determine the equations of the tangent and the normal to the curve at the point $(3, 4)$.

2 Find the equations of the tangent to the curve $y^2 = (1 + x)^2(3 - x)$ at the points P and Q where $x = 1$. If PQ intersects the x-axis at S and the tangents intersect at T, find the length of ST.

3 Show that the curves $y = x^2$ and $6y = 7 - x^3$ intersect at the point $(1, 1)$. Show also that the tangents to the curves at this point are at right angles.

4 The parametric equations of a curve are

$$x = 3(2\theta - \sin 2\theta), y = 3(1 - \cos 2\theta).$$

The tangent and the normal to the curve at the point P, where $\theta = \pi/4$, meet the y-axis at L and M respectively. Show that the area of triangle PLM is $9(\pi - 2)^2/4$.

5 Show that the equation of the tangent at any point 't' on the curve $x = 2 \cos t - \cos 2t$, $y = 2 \sin t - \sin 2t$ is

$$x \sin(3t/2) - y \cos(3t/2) = 3 \sin(t/2).$$

Prove that the tangents at the points t and $t + \pi$ are perpendicular to each other.

6 Find the equation of the tangent to the curve $3y^2 = x^2(x + 1)$ at the point $P(2, 2)$. If this tangent meets the curve again at Q, find the coordinates of Q and show that PQ is normal to the curve at Q.

7 The curve whose equation is $y = e^x(ax^2 + bx + c)$, where a, b, c are constants, is such that its tangents are parallel to the x-axis at $x = 1$ and $x = 3$ and the curve cuts the y-axis where $y = 9$. Calculate a, b and c. (L)

8 Find the equation of the tangent to the curve $3y^2 = 2x^3 + x^2$ at the point $A(1, 1)$. Show that this tangent meets the curve again at the point B whose abscissa is $1/6$ and find the ordinate of B. (L)

9 A curve joining the points $(0, 1)$ and $(0, -1)$ is represented by the equation

$y^2 = (1 + x)^2(1 - x^2)$ where $x > 0$. Find $\dfrac{dy}{dx}$ in terms of x and y, and hence determine

the coordinates of the points on the curve at which the tangent is parallel to the x-axis and of the point at which the tangent is perpendicular to the x-axis. Sketch the curve.

3.3 Newton–Raphson formula for the iteration to roots of an equation

Usually a tangent to the curve $y = f(x)$ can be used to determine more accurate approximations to a root of the equation $f(x) = 0$ than a given first approximation, say $x = x_1$.

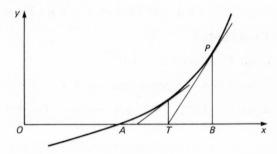

Fig. 3.2

Suppose the graph of $y = f(x)$ is as shown in Fig. 3.2, cutting the x-axis at the point A. Then $x = OA$ is a root of the equation $f(x) = 0$. Suppose, further, that $x = x_1$ is a given first approximation to this root, where $OB = x_1$. If the ordinate is drawn through B, cutting the curve at P, then in general, provided B is sufficiently close to A, the tangent to the curve $y = f(x)$ at P will cut the x-axis at a point T, which will lie closer to A than does the point B. Hence $x = x_2 = OT$ is a second and better approximation to the root $x = OA$ than is $x = x_1$.

Now

$$x_2 = OT = OB - TB = x_1 - \frac{BP}{\tan PTB}.$$

But $BP = f(x_1)$ and $\tan PTB = f'(x_1)$,

$$\Rightarrow x_2 = OT = x_1 - \frac{f(x_1)}{f'(x_1)}.$$

The process can be repeated to give a third approximation

$$x_3 = x_2 - \frac{f(x_2)}{f'(x_2)}$$

and so on. This formula is known as the *Newton–Raphson* or *Newton formula*. Its use depends upon the first approximation being sufficiently close to the true value to ensure that the tangent at P cuts the x-axis at a point T which is closer to the position A of the true root than is B, the position of the first approximation. This may not happen, as shown in Fig. 3.3, if the first approximation is not a sufficiently good approximation.

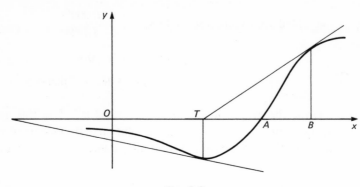

Fig. 3.3

Example 3   Show that a root of the equation $\tan \theta = 1 + \sin \theta$ occurs in the vicinity of $\theta = 1\cdot08$ rad. Use this value as a first approximation to calculate the value of this root correct to three decimal places.

Many students attempting to show that the equation $\tan \theta = 1 + \sin \theta$ has a root in the vicinity of $\theta = 1\cdot08$ simply substitute this value into the equation. They believe that because the LHS turns out to be approximately equal to the RHS the equation must therefore have a root near to $\theta = 1\cdot08$. Such an argument is spurious and proves nothing – the student should proceed as follows.
   Let $y = f(\theta) = 1 + \sin \theta - \tan \theta$.

$$f(1\cdot07) = 1 + 0\cdot8772 - 1\cdot8270 = +0\cdot0502,$$

$$f(1\cdot09) = 1 + 0\cdot8866 - 1\cdot9171 = -0\cdot0305.$$

Hence, since the function $f(\theta) = 1 + \sin \theta - \tan \theta$ is continuous for $1\cdot07 < \theta < 1\cdot09$, the curve $y = 1 + \sin \theta - \tan \theta$ crosses the θ-axis between $\theta = 1\cdot07$ and $\theta = 1\cdot09 \Rightarrow$ the equation $\tan \theta = 1 + \sin \theta$ has a root in the vicinity of $\theta = 1\cdot08$.

First approximation $\theta_1 = 1\cdot08.$

$$f(1 \cdot 08) = 1 + 0 \cdot 8820 - 1 \cdot 8712 = 0 \cdot 0108.$$

$$f'(\theta) = \cos \theta - \sec^2 \theta$$

$$\Rightarrow f'(1 \cdot 08) = 0 \cdot 4713 - 4 \cdot 5015 = -4 \cdot 0302$$

$$\Rightarrow \text{Second approximation} = 1 \cdot 08 - \frac{0 \cdot 0108}{(-4 \cdot 0302)}$$

$$= 1 \cdot 08 + 0 \cdot 002680 \approx 1 \cdot 0827.$$

$$f(1 \cdot 0827) = 1 + 0 \cdot 8832 - 1 \cdot 8834 = -0 \cdot 0002$$

$$f'(1 \cdot 0827) = 0 \cdot 4689 - 4 \cdot 5473 = -4 \cdot 0784$$

$$\Rightarrow \text{Third approximation} = 1 \cdot 0827 - \frac{(-0 \cdot 0002)}{(-4 \cdot 0784)}$$

$$= 1 \cdot 0827 - 0 \cdot 000049$$

$$= 1 \cdot 083 \text{ to 3 decimal places.}$$

Example 4 Draw the graph of $y = \cos x$, $0 \leqslant x \leqslant \pi/2$. Use this graph to show that the equation $2 \cos x - x = 0$ has a solution in the vicinity of $x = 1 \cdot 0$. Apply Newton's Method to obtain a second approximation to this root.

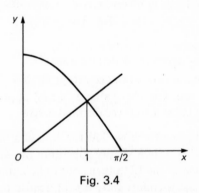

Fig. 3.4

The graph of $y = \cos x$, $0 \leqslant x \leqslant \pi/2$, is as shown in Fig. 3.4. The equation to be solved, $2 \cos x - x = 0$, can be written in the form $\cos x = x/2$. Now the curves $y = \cos x$ and $y = x/2$ will intersect where they have the same value of y, i.e. where $y = \cos x = x/2$. Hence it is necessary to draw, using the same axes, the straight line $y = x/2$. The value of x where this straight line meets the curve $y = \cos x$ will then give a solution of the equation $2 \cos x - x = 0$. This can be seen to be in the vicinity of $x = 1 \cdot 0$.

Let $f(x) = 2 \cos x - x$

Then $$f'(x) = -2 \sin x - 1$$

$$\Rightarrow \text{Second approximation} = 1{\cdot}0 - \frac{f(1{\cdot}0)}{f'(1{\cdot}0)}$$

$$= 1{\cdot}0 - \frac{2 \cos 1{\cdot}0 - 1{\cdot}0}{-2 \sin 1{\cdot}0 - 1}$$

$$= 1{\cdot}0 - \frac{2 \times 0{\cdot}5403 - 1{\cdot}0}{-2 \times 0{\cdot}8415 - 1}$$

$$= 1{\cdot}0 + \frac{0{\cdot}0806}{2{\cdot}6830}$$

$$= 1{\cdot}0 + 0{\cdot}0300 = 1{\cdot}03 \text{ (to 3 significant figures)}.$$

Exercise 3.3

1 If $x = a_1$ is an approximation to a root of $f(x) = 0$ then in general a better approximation a_2 is given by Newton's Rule,

$$a_2 = a_1 - \frac{f(a_1)}{f'(a_1)}.$$

By means of a sketch in each case, illustrate a situation
 (i) where Newton's rule yields a better approximation,
 (ii) where it does not.
   By means of a sketch, or otherwise, find an approximation to the non-zero root of

$$\sin x - 2x^2 = 0.$$

Find this root correct to two decimal places.   (L)

2 Prove, graphically or otherwise, that the equation

$$x + \sin x = 1,$$

where x is measured in radians, has one real root. Calculate this root correct to two places of decimals.

3 Taking $1{\cdot}55$ as a first approximation to a root of the equation $x - 2 + \ln x = 0$, use one application of the Newton–Raphson method to obtain a second approximation.   (L)

4 Show, graphically or otherwise, that the equation $x^4 - 6x - 3 = 0$ has two real roots and two only, one between -1 and 0, the other between 1 and 2.
   By any method of approximation, obtain the negative root correct to three significant figures.   (L)

5 By means of sketch graphs, or otherwise, show that the equation

$$x^2 \sin x = 1$$

has an infinite number of real roots. If $x = n\pi$ is a first approximation to a root, where n is a positive or negative integer, show that an improved approximation is $n\pi + (-1)^n/(n^2\pi^2)$.

6 By drawing appropriate graphs show that the equation

$$x(\pi - x) = 4 \sin 2x$$

has four real roots. Show that the root between $x = 0$ and $x = \pi$ occurs at approximately $x = 1.2$ and by means of a single application of Newton's method determine a more accurate estimate of its value. (AEB)

7 By sketching the graphs of $y = e^x - 3$ and $y = \ln(x + 3)$, show that the equation $e^x - \ln(x + 3) = 3$ has two real roots. Use the Newton-Raphson method once to improve the approximation to the positive root, taking 1.5 as the initial value of x. (L)

8 The volume of a closed cylindrical drum is V cm^3 and its total surface area is A cm^2. Show that the radius r cm can be found from the equation

$$\pi r^3 - \tfrac{1}{2}Ar + V = 0.$$

If $V = A = 200$ show that one root of the equation in r is approximately 2.5. Using this approximation, calculate the value of the root correct to three significant figures. (AEB)

3.4   Rates of change

If $y = f(x)$, then $\dfrac{dy}{dx}$ is a measure of the rate of change of y with respect to x.

Thus, for a body moving in a straight line so that its distance is s from a fixed point at time t, where $s = f(t)$, then the *velocity* of the body is *defined* as the rate of change of distance s with respect to time t

$$\Rightarrow \text{velocity} = \frac{ds}{dt} = f'(t) = v, \quad \text{say.}$$

Now the *acceleration* of the body is *defined* as the rate of change of velocity v of the body with respect to time t

$$\Rightarrow \text{acceleration} = \frac{dv}{dt} = a, \quad \text{say.}$$

Since $v = \dfrac{ds}{dt} = f'(t)$, the acceleration $\dfrac{dv}{dt}$ can be expressed in alternative forms thus:

$$\text{acceleration} = a = \frac{dv}{dt} = \frac{d}{dt}\left(\frac{ds}{dt}\right) = \frac{d^2 s}{dt^2} = f''(t).$$

Alternatively, using the chain rule,

$$a = \frac{dv}{dt} = \frac{dv}{ds}\cdot\frac{ds}{dt} = \frac{dv}{ds}\cdot v$$

$$\Rightarrow a = \frac{dv}{dt} = \frac{d^2 s}{dt^2} = v\frac{dv}{ds} = f''(t).$$

Derivatives with respect to time t are so important and occur so frequently that mathematicians often choose to use a special notation – the dot notation – for derivatives with respect to this variable.

Thus
$$s = f(t) \Rightarrow v = \frac{ds}{dt} = \dot{s},$$

$$a = \frac{dv}{dt} = \frac{d^2s}{dt^2} \Rightarrow a = \dot{v} = \ddot{s}.$$

Example 5 A particle is projected vertically upwards with a speed of 49 m s^{-1} reaching a height $s = 49t - 4{\cdot}9t^2$ metres at the end of t seconds. Find the height to which the particle rises and determine its velocity when its height is 78·4 m.

$$s = 49t - 4{\cdot}9t^2 \Rightarrow v = 49 - 9{\cdot}8t.$$

When $v = 0$, $49 - 9{\cdot}8t = 0 \Rightarrow t = 5.$
For maximum height, $v = 0$ and $s = 49.5 - 4{\cdot}9.5^2 = 122{\cdot}5$
$\Rightarrow$ particle reaches a height of 122·5 m.
When the height of the particle is 78·4 m, the time t is given by

$$78{\cdot}4 = 49t - 4{\cdot}9t^2$$

$$\Leftrightarrow t^2 - 10t + 16 = 0$$

$$\Leftrightarrow (t - 2)(t - 8) = 0$$

$$\Leftrightarrow t = 2 \quad \text{or} \quad 8.$$

When $t = 2, \dfrac{ds}{dt} = 49 - 9{\cdot}8.2 = 49 - 19{\cdot}6 = 29{\cdot}4.$

$t = 2 \Rightarrow$ velocity of the particle is 29·4 m s^{-1} upwards.

When $t = 8, \dfrac{ds}{dt} = 49 - 9{\cdot}8.8 = 49 - 78{\cdot}4 = -29{\cdot}4.$

$t = 8 \Rightarrow$ velocity of the particle is 29·4 m s^{-1} downwards.

Example 6 A man of height 2 m walks at the rate of $1\frac{2}{3}$ m s^{-1} towards a street lamp which is 7 m above the ground. At what rate is (i) the tip of his shadow moving, (ii) the length of his shadow changing?

At time t s let the man be x m from the foot of the lamp post, whilst the tip of his shadow is y m from the foot of the lamp post as shown in Fig. 3.5.

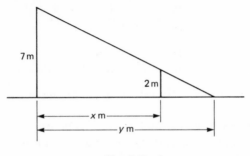

Fig. 3.5

From similar triangles $y/7 = (y - x)/2 \Rightarrow 5y = 7x$.
Differentiating with respect to time t,

$$5\frac{dy}{dt} = 7\frac{dx}{dt}.$$

But $\qquad \dfrac{dx}{dt} = -\dfrac{5}{3} \Rightarrow \dfrac{dy}{dt} = \dfrac{7}{5}\dfrac{dx}{dt} = \dfrac{7}{5}\cdot\left(-\dfrac{5}{3}\right) = -2\tfrac{1}{3}$

$\Rightarrow$ the tip of his shadow is moving at $2\tfrac{1}{3}$ m s^{-1}, the negative sign indicating that it is moving towards the lamp post.
Let l = length of shadow. Then

$$l = y - x \Rightarrow \frac{dl}{dt} = \frac{dy}{dt} - \frac{dx}{dt}$$

$$\Rightarrow \frac{dl}{dt} = -\frac{7}{3} + \frac{5}{3} = -\frac{2}{3}.$$

$\Rightarrow$ length of the shadow is decreasing at $\tfrac{2}{3}$ m s^{-1}.

In dealing with problems involving rates of change it is often necessary to apply the chain rule.

Example 7 A hemispherical bowl, of radius a cm and with its axis vertical, is being filled with water at a steady rate of $5\pi a^3$ cm^3 per minute. Find, in cm per minute, the rate at which the level is rising when the depth of water is $\tfrac{1}{3} a$ cm. [The volume of a cap, of height h cm, of a sphere of radius r cm is $\tfrac{1}{3}\pi h^2(3r - h)$ cm^3.]

When the depth of water is h cm the volume of water is V cm^3, where $V = \tfrac{1}{3}\pi h^2(3a - h)$,

$$\Rightarrow \frac{dV}{dh} = \frac{1}{3}\pi(6ah - 3h^2) \Rightarrow \frac{dh}{dV} = \frac{3}{\pi(6ah - 3h^2)}.$$

But $\dfrac{dV}{dt} = 5\pi a^3 \Rightarrow$ rate at which water level is rising is $\dfrac{dh}{dt} = \dfrac{dh}{dV}\dfrac{dV}{dt}$

$$\Rightarrow \frac{dh}{dt} = \frac{3}{\pi[6ah - 3h^2]}\cdot 5\pi a^3.$$

When $h = \tfrac{1}{3}a$, $\qquad \dfrac{dh}{dt} = \dfrac{15a^3}{6a.(a/3) - 3.(a/3)^2} = \dfrac{15a}{2 - \tfrac{1}{3}} = 9a$

$\Rightarrow$ the water level is rising at the rate of $9a$ cm per minute.

Example 8 A block of ice in the form of a cube melts in such a way that it remains cubical and its volume decreases at a constant rate. At 1200 hours the length of an edge of the cube is 2 m and at 1900 hours on the same day its edge

34 *Differentiation*

is of length 1 m. Calculate, in m^2 per hour, the rate of decrease of the surface area of the cube when its edge is of length 1·6 m.

At 1200 hours the volume of the cube of ice is 2^3 m^3.

At 1900 hours the volume of the cube of ice is 1^3 m^3.

$\Rightarrow$ Rate of change of volume $= \dfrac{1^3 - 2^3}{7} m^3 h^{-1} = -1\ m^3 h^{-1} \Rightarrow \dfrac{dV}{dt} = -1.$

When the side of the cube is x m the volume $V = x^3$ m^3 and the surface area $A = 6x^2$ m^2

$$\Rightarrow \frac{dV}{dx} = 3x^2 \quad \text{and} \quad \frac{dA}{dx} = 12x.$$

Hence $\qquad \dfrac{dA}{dt} = \dfrac{dA}{dx} \cdot \dfrac{dx}{dV} \cdot \dfrac{dV}{dt} = 12x \cdot \dfrac{1}{3x^2} \cdot (-1) = \dfrac{-4}{x}$

$$\Rightarrow \text{when } x = 1\cdot6, \frac{dA}{dt} = \frac{-4}{1\cdot6} = -2\cdot5$$

$\Rightarrow$ when the edge is of length 1·6 m the surface area of the cube is decreasing at 2·5 m^2 per hour.

Exercise 3.4

1 The volume of water in a vessel is $x(49 + x^2)$ m^3 when the depth of the water is x m. If water is poured into the vessel at the constant rate of 8 m^3 per minute, calculate, in cm per minute, correct to two significant figures, the rate at which the level of the water is rising in the vessel when the depth is 4 m.

2 The ends A and B of a rod of length 8 cm move along two grooves Ox and Oy respectively, which are at right angles. If A moves at 5 $cm\,s^{-1}$, find the speed of B when $OA = 4$ cm.

3 A horizontal trough of length 2 m is closed at both ends and is 1 m deep. Its cross-section is an isosceles triangle of base (upwards) 0·6 m. Water runs into the trough at the rate of 0·02 $m^3\,s^{-1}$. Find the rate at which the water level is rising when the height of the water is 0·5 m.

4 A boy is standing on a bank at the side of a pond sailing his yacht. He pulls the yacht towards him by means of a string which he is pulling in at the rate of 5 $cm\,s^{-1}$. Find the speed of the yacht when the length of string out is 12·5 m and the boy's hands are 3·5 m above the level of the yacht.

5 A particle P moves in a straight line so that t seconds after passing through a fixed point A, the distance AP is x m, where x is given by $x = \ln(1 + t^3) + (1 + at)^n + k$ and a, n, and k are constants. If the velocity and acceleration of the particle at A are 2 $m\,s^{-1}$ and 1 $m\,s^{-2}$ respectively, find the numerical values of a, n and k.

6 Points U, V lie on the axis Ox at distances u cm, v cm respectively from O and

$$\frac{1}{u} + \frac{1}{v} = \frac{1}{f},$$

where f is a positive constant and $u > 0$, $v > 0$. The point U moves along Ox, in the direction of x increasing, with speed $\dfrac{1}{4}f$ $cm\,s^{-1}$. Show that U and V always move in opposite directions and calculate, in magnitude and direction, the velocity of V when $u = 3f$. (L)

7 The point P moves in such a way that at time t its cartesian coordinates with respect to an origin O are

$$x = e^{-t}, y = 2te^{-t}.$$

The distance OP is denoted by r and the angle between OP and the x-axis by θ. Find in terms of t
(i) the rate of change of r^2 with respect to t,
(ii) the rate of change of θ with respect to t. (L)

8 The height h and the base radius r of a right circular cone vary in such a way that the volume remains constant. Find the rate of change of h with respect to r at the instant when h and r are equal.

9 The volume of a sphere is increasing at the constant rate of $100 \text{ m}^3 \text{ s}^{-1}$. Find the rate of increase of the surface area at the instant when the radius is 50 m. Find also the radius of the surface when the surface area is increasing at the rate of $40 \text{ m}^2 \text{ s}^{-1}$.

3.5 Small increments

If $y = f(x)$ and δy is the small increment in y corresponding to a small incremental change δx in x, then $\dfrac{dy}{dx} = \lim\limits_{\delta x \to 0} \dfrac{\delta y}{\delta x}$. Hence when δx is very small $\dfrac{\delta y}{\delta x} \approx \dfrac{dy}{dx}$

and so

$$\delta y \approx \frac{dy}{dx}.\delta x = f'(x)\delta x.$$

This result can be used to determine the approximate change in the value of a function due to a small change in its dependent variable.

Example 9   The volume of a sphere is increased from $972\pi \text{ cm}^3$ to $973\pi \text{ cm}^3$. Calculate the increase in the radius of the sphere.

Let the volume and radius of the sphere be V cm and r cm respectively.

$$V = 972\pi \Rightarrow \frac{4}{3}\pi r^3 = 972\pi \Rightarrow r^3 = 729 \Rightarrow r = 9.$$

$$V = \frac{4}{3}\pi r^3 \Rightarrow \frac{dV}{dr} = 4\pi r^2.$$

$$\delta V \approx \frac{dV}{dr}\delta r, \quad \delta V = \pi \Rightarrow 4\pi r^2 \delta r = \pi$$

and, as $r = 9$, $\delta r = 1/(4.9^2) \approx 0.0031$ cm

$\Rightarrow$ the radius of the sphere increases by 0.0031 cm.

Example 10   Given that the radius of a sphere decreases by 0.15%, use differentiation to estimate the corresponding percentage decrease in
(a) the volume of the sphere,
(b) the surface area of the sphere.

(a) The radius r of the sphere increases by $-0.15\% \Rightarrow \delta r = -0.0015r$
$\Rightarrow$ the volume V of the sphere increases by

$$\delta V \approx \frac{dV}{dr}\delta r = 4\pi r^2 \delta r$$

$$= 4\pi r^2 . (-0.0015r) = -0.006\pi r^3$$

$$\Rightarrow \frac{\delta V}{V} = \frac{-0.006\pi r^3}{\frac{4}{3}\pi r^3} = -0.0045$$

$\Rightarrow$ percentage decrease in the volume of 0.45.

(b) The surface area A of the sphere increases by $\delta A \approx \dfrac{dA}{dr}\delta r$

$$A = 4\pi r^2 \Rightarrow \frac{dA}{dr} = 8\pi r$$

$$\Rightarrow \delta A \approx 8\pi r \delta r = 8\pi r . (-0.0015r)$$

$$\Rightarrow \frac{\delta A}{A} \approx \frac{-0.012\pi r^2}{4\pi r^2} = -0.003$$

$\Rightarrow$ percentage decrease in the surface area of 0.3.

3.6 Errors

Numerical results are normally calculated from given data by means of mathematical formulae. For example, the volume V of a sphere of radius r can be determined by substituting the value of r in $V = 4\pi r^3/3$. If r is measured incorrectly, then obviously V will be in error. The *error* is approximately $\delta V = \dfrac{dV}{dr}\delta r$, where δr is the error or estimated error in r.

Generally, more interest is shown in the *relative* or *proportional error* (i.e. the ratio of the error to the calculated value) or the *percentage error* than in the actual error.

Example 11   The acceleration g due to gravity is determined by measuring the time of oscillation t of a simple pendulum of length l and using the relationship $t = 2\pi\sqrt{(l/g)}$. Calculate (a) the proportional error, (b) the percentage error, in g if the observed value of t is 0.2 per cent too large.

$$t = 2\pi\sqrt{\left(\frac{l}{g}\right)} \Rightarrow g = \frac{4\pi^2 l}{t^2} \quad \text{and} \quad \frac{dg}{dt} = \frac{-8\pi^2 l}{t^3}$$

$$\Rightarrow \delta g \approx \frac{-8\pi^2 l}{t^3}\delta t$$

$$\Rightarrow \frac{\delta g}{g} \approx \frac{-8\pi^2 l}{t^3} . \frac{t^2}{4\pi^2 l}\delta t = \frac{-2}{t}\delta t.$$

Error in t, 0.2 per cent too large $\Rightarrow \delta t = \dfrac{+0.2t}{100}$.

(a) Proportional error $= \dfrac{\delta g}{g} \approx \dfrac{-2}{t} \cdot \left(\dfrac{0.2t}{100}\right) = \dfrac{-0.4}{100} = -\dfrac{1}{250}$

$\Rightarrow$ calculated value of g is too small by about $1/250$ of its calculated value.

(b) Percentage error in $g = \dfrac{\delta g}{g} \times 100 \approx \dfrac{-100}{250} = -0.4$

$\Rightarrow$ calculated value of g is 0.4% too small.

Logarithms can be used with advantage in problems involving small increments and errors. Suppose that $y = u_1 u_2 \ldots u_m$. Then

$$\ln y = \ln u_1 + \ln u_2 + \ldots + \ln u_m.$$

Taking small increments of both sides of this equation, and using

$$\delta(\ln x) \approx \frac{\mathrm{d}}{\mathrm{d}x}(\ln x)\delta x = \frac{\delta x}{x},$$

$$\Rightarrow \frac{\delta y}{y} \approx \frac{\delta u_1}{u_1} + \frac{\delta u_2}{u_2} + \ldots + \frac{\delta u_m}{u_m}.$$

Example 12 Suppose that $V = \sin 2x \tan 3y$ and x, y are subject to small errors δx, δy respectively. Then the corresponding proportional error $(\delta V/V)$ in V is obtained as follows:

$$V = \sin 2x \tan 3y$$

$$\Rightarrow \ln V = \ln \sin 2x + \ln \tan 3y$$

$$\Rightarrow \frac{\delta V}{V} \approx \frac{\mathrm{d}}{\mathrm{d}x}(\ln \sin 2x)\delta x + \frac{\mathrm{d}}{\mathrm{d}y}(\ln \tan 3y)\delta y$$

$$\Rightarrow \frac{\delta V}{V} \approx 2\delta x \cot 2x + 3\delta y \sec^2 3y \cot 3y.$$

Exercise 3.6

1 A coat of paint of thickness 0.01 cm is applied to a cube of edge 20 cm. Use the method of small increments to find approximately the number of cubic centimetres of paint used. Compare your answer with the exact amount used.
2 Use $\sqrt[6]{(64)}$ to find an approximate value of $\sqrt[6]{(65)}$.
3 The weight of a body varies inversely as the square of its distance from the centre of the earth. If the earth's radius is 4000 miles, find the approximate weight of a woman 120 miles above the earth's surface if her weight at the surface is 160 pounds.
4 The specific gravity s of a body is calculated from its weights w_1 and w_2 in air and water, respectively, from the formula

$$s = \frac{w_1}{w_1 - w_2},$$

where $w_1 > w_2 > 0$. If w_2 is accurately measured but there is a small error δw_1 in the measurement of w_1, show that the error in the calculated value of s is approximately

$$-\frac{w_2 \delta w_1}{(w_1 - w_2)^2}.$$ (L)

5   The density ρ of a uniform solid right circular cylinder, of mass M, radius r and length l, is calculated from the formula $M = \pi r^2 l \rho$. If the measured mass is 2% too large, the measured radius is 3% too small and the measured length is 1% too large, calculate the percentage error in the calculated density. (L)

6   The radius r of a circular cylinder, of volume V and length l, is calculated from the formula $V = \pi r^2 l$. If the measured volume is 3% too large and the measured length 2% too small, find an approximation to the percentage error in the calculated radius. (L)

7   The area of a certain triangle is calculated from the formula $\Delta = \frac{1}{2}ab \sin C$. If the sides a, b are measured correctly, but an error of $1°50'$ is made in taking the angle C to be $54°12'$, find, to two significant figures, the resulting error in Δ as a fraction of its calculated value. (L)

8   The area Δ of a triangle is calculated from the formula $\Delta = \frac{1}{2}ab \sin C$. Calculate, correct to two significant figures, an approximate value for the percentage error in Δ which results from errors of -0.1 cm in a, $+0.3$ cm in b and $+30'$ in C when the correct values of a, b, and C are 12 cm, 14 cm, and $45°$ respectively. (L)

3.7   Further geometrical consideration of differentiation

It has already been stated that $\dfrac{dy}{dx}$ is the gradient of the tangent to the curve $y = f(x)$ at the point (x, y) on the curve, i.e. $\dfrac{dy}{dx} = \tan \psi$, where ψ is the angle contained between the tangent to the curve at the point (x, y) and the positive direction of the x-axis.

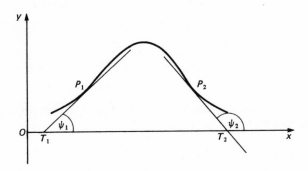

Fig. 3.6

Thus, if the curve $y = f(x)$ is as shown in Fig. 3.6, then at P_1, $\dfrac{dy}{dx} = \tan P_1 T_1 x$ or $\tan \psi_1$, where ψ_1 is an acute angle, so that $\tan \psi_1$ and $\dfrac{dy}{dx}$ are both positive.

However, at P_2, $\dfrac{dy}{dx} = \tan P_2 T_2 x = \tan \psi_2$, where ψ_2 is an obtuse angle,

so that $\tan \psi_2$ and $\dfrac{dy}{dx}$ are both negative.

The geometrical implications of these results are: if ψ is to be an acute angle, then the graph of $y = f(x)$ must be such that as x increases y increases, if ψ is to be an obtuse angle, then the graph of $y = f(x)$ must be such that as x increases y decreases, as illustrated in Figs. 3.7 and 3.8.

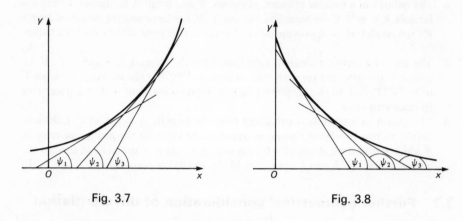

Fig. 3.7   Fig. 3.8

Alternatively: a function $f(x)$ increases when x increases if $f'(x)$ is positive. A function $f(x)$ decreases when x increases if $f'(x)$ is negative.

Example 13   Show that, for $x > 0$, the function $x - \ln(1 + x)$ is positive and increases with x.

Let $f(x) = x - \ln(1 + x)$.
We need to show that $f(x)$ is positive for $x > 0$.
Now $f(0) = 0 - \ln(1) = 0$.

Further, $f'(x) = 1 - \dfrac{1}{1 + x} = \dfrac{x}{1 + x}$ and therefore, if x is positive, $f'(x)$ is positive.

Hence, as x increases, $f(x)$ increases $\Rightarrow f(x) = x - \ln(1 + x)$ is positive for $x > 0$ and increases with x.

Example 14   Show that, for $x > 0$, $x > \sin x > x - x^3/6$.

Let $f(x) = x - \sin x \Rightarrow f(0) = 0$.
$f'(x) = 1 - \cos x > 0$ for all positive x except when $x = 2r\pi$, $r \in \mathbb{N}$.
But $\sin 2r\pi = 0$, $r \in \mathbb{N}$. Hence, for $x > 0$, $f(x) > 0$.

$$\Rightarrow x - \sin x > 0 \Leftrightarrow x > \sin x \text{ for } x > 0.$$

Let $g(x) = \sin x - x + x^3/6 \Rightarrow g(0) = 0$.

$g'(x) = \cos x - 1 + x^2/2$ which we need to show is positive for $x > 0$.
$g''(x) = -\sin x + x > 0$ for $x > 0$ as shown above, and, since $g'(0) = 0$,

$$g'(x) > 0 \text{ for } x > 0.$$

Hence $g(0) = 0$ and $g'(x) > 0 \Rightarrow g(x) > 0$ for $x > 0$

$$\Rightarrow \sin x - x + x^3/6 > 0 \Leftrightarrow \sin x > x - x^3/6.$$

Hence, for $x > 0$, $\qquad x > \sin x > x - x^3/6.$

Exercise 3.7

1 Show that, for all values of θ greater than zero, $3\theta + 8\cos(\theta/2) - \sin\theta$ is positive.
2 If $f(x) = x - \sin x$, prove that $f'(x) \geqslant 0$ for all real x and deduce that $x \geqslant \sin x$ for all $x \geqslant 0$.
   Show in a similar fashion that, when $x \geqslant 0$,

$$x\cos x - \sin x + \frac{1}{3}x^3 \geqslant 0.$$

3 Show that the function $\sin\theta - \theta\cos\theta$ increases steadily as θ increases from 0 to $\frac{1}{2}\pi$, and hence deduce that the function $\theta/\sin\theta$ increases as θ increases from 0 to $\frac{1}{2}\pi$.   (L)
4 The function $f(x)$ is defined for all $x \geqslant 0$ by

$$f(x) = \tfrac{1}{2}x - \tfrac{1}{4}x^2 + \tfrac{1}{2}(x^2 - 1)\ln(1 + x).$$

   Find the derived function $f'(x)$ and deduce that $f(x) \geqslant 0$ for all $x \geqslant 0$.   (L)
5 Show that, if $x > 0$,

$$x - \tfrac{1}{2}x^2 < \ln(1 + x) < x - \tfrac{1}{2}x^2 + \tfrac{1}{3}x^3.$$

6 Show that, if $x > 0$,

$$x > \tan^{-1} x > x - \tfrac{1}{3}x^3.$$

3.8   Stationary points

Consider a function $f(x)$ whose graph is shown in Fig. 3.9.

At all points on the curve between A and B the tangent to the curve makes an angle ψ_1 with the positive direction of the x-axis such that ψ_1 is an acute angle. Hence $\tan\psi_1 > 0 \Rightarrow f'(x) > 0$.

At all points between B and C the tangent to the curve makes an obtuse angle ψ_2 with the positive direction of the x-axis. Hence, in this case $\tan\psi_2 < 0 \Rightarrow f'(x) < 0$.

Similarly, at all points on the curve between C and D and between D and E, ψ is acute and therefore $f'(x) > 0$. At the points B, C and D the tangent to the curve is parallel to the x-axis. Hence, at B, C and D angle $\psi = 0$ and therefore at these points $f'(x) = 0$ also. We shall mark the sign of $f'(x)$ on the curve as shown in Fig. 3.10.

Between A and B the function $f(x)$ increases as x increases. At B, $f(x)$ stops increasing momentarily as x increases and then, between B and C, $f(x)$ decreases as x increases. At C, $f(x)$ stops decreasing momentarily as x increases and then, between C and D, $f(x)$ increases as x increases. At D, the function again

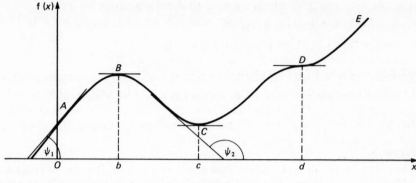

Fig. 3.9

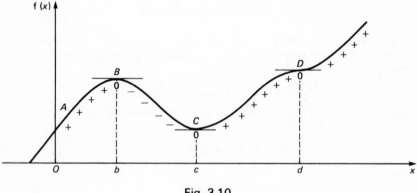

Fig. 3.10

momentarily stops increasing as x increases and then between D and E it again increases as x increases.

Points such as B, C and D, where $f'(x) = 0$ and therefore where the function is neither increasing nor decreasing, are called *stationary points*. Stationary points fall into the following three categories.

1. Maximum   A *maximum* is the value of the function at a point where $f'(x) = 0$ and $f'(x)$ changes from positive to negative for values of x just less and just greater respectively than that for which $f'(x) = 0$, i.e. as x goes through the point.

2. Minimum   A *minimum* is the value of the function at a point where $f'(x) = 0$ and $f'(x)$ changes from negative to positive for values of x just less and just greater respectively than that for which $f'(x) = 0$, i.e. as x goes through the point.

3. Inflexion with horizontal tangent   is a point where $f'(x) = 0$ but where $f'(x)$ does not change sign as x increases through the point where $f'(x) = 0$.

Hence for the function $y = f(x)$ shown in Fig. 3.9 there is

(i) a maximum value at the point B,

(ii) a minimum value at the point C,

(iii) an inflexion with a horizontal tangent at the point D.

It should be noted that maximum or minimum values are not the greatest and least values respectively that the function can possess in an interval (a, b). In fact they are only the greatest and least values in the neighbourhood of the point concerned. Consequently, to avoid any misunderstanding they are often called 'local' maximum and 'local' minimum values.

Example 15 Find the maximum and minimum values of the function $\dfrac{x^2}{(x + 1)^3}$

and distinguish between them.

$$y = \frac{x^2}{(x + 1)^3} \Rightarrow \frac{dy}{dx} = \frac{(x + 1)^3 \cdot 2x - x^2 \cdot 3(x + 1)^2}{(x + 1)^6} = \frac{x(2 - x)}{(x + 1)^4}.$$

For a stationary point $\dfrac{dy}{dx} = 0$

$$\Rightarrow \frac{x(2 - x)}{(x + 1)^4} = 0 \Rightarrow x = 0 \text{ or } x = 2.$$

Test

If $-1 < x < 0$, $\dfrac{dy}{dx} = \dfrac{(-\text{ve}) \times (+\text{ve})}{(+\text{ve})} = (-\text{ve})$,

If $\;\;0 < x < 2$, $\dfrac{dy}{dx} = \dfrac{(+\text{ve}) \times (+\text{ve})}{(+\text{ve})} = (+\text{ve})$.

$\dfrac{dy}{dx}$ changes sign from $(-\text{ve})$ to $(+\text{ve})$ as x passes through $x = 0$

$\Rightarrow$ minimum value occurs when $x = 0 \Rightarrow$ minimum value $= 0$.

If $0 < x < 2$, $\dfrac{dy}{dx} = \dfrac{(+\text{ve}) \times (+\text{ve})}{(+\text{ve})} = (+\text{ve})$,

if $x > 2$, $\dfrac{dy}{dx} = \dfrac{(+\text{ve}) \times (-\text{ve})}{(+\text{ve})} = (-\text{ve})$.

$\dfrac{dy}{dx}$ changes sign from $(+\text{ve})$ to $(-\text{ve})$ as x passes through $x = 2$

$\Rightarrow$ maximum occurs when $x = 2 \Rightarrow$ maximum value $= 2^2/3^3 = 4/27$.

Note that, since $f'(x)$ does not change sign between consecutive zeros, it is sufficient, in this case, to consider its sign at $x = 1$ in order to establish that $f'(x) > 0$ for $0 < x < 2$.

If one is asked to sketch the graph of a function, the determination of maximum and minimum values is often of great assistance.

Example 16   Find the maximum value of the function xe^{-x} and sketch the graph of $y = xe^{-x}$.

$$y = xe^{-x} \Rightarrow \frac{dy}{dx} = x(-e^{-x}) + 1.e^{-x} = e^{-x}(1 - x).$$

For a stationary value $\dfrac{dy}{dx} = 0$

$$\Rightarrow e^{-x}(1 - x) = 0 \Rightarrow x = 1 \text{ since } e^{-x} \neq 0.$$

Test

If $x < 1, \dfrac{dy}{dx} = (+\text{ve}) \times (+\text{ve}) = (+\text{ve}),$

If $x > 1, \dfrac{dy}{dx} = (+\text{ve}) \times (-\text{ve}) = (-\text{ve}),$

$\Rightarrow \dfrac{dy}{dx}$ changes sign from $(+\text{ve})$ to $(-\text{ve})$ as x passes through $x = 1$

$\Rightarrow$ maximum occurs when $x = 1 \Rightarrow$ maximum value $= e^{-1}.$

When $x = 0, y = 0.$

When $x \rightarrow +\infty,$ $\qquad y \rightarrow \lim_{x \to \infty} \dfrac{x}{e^x} = \lim_{x \to \infty} \dfrac{x}{1 + x/1! + x^2/2! + \ldots} = 0.$

When $x \rightarrow -\infty,$ $\qquad y \rightarrow \lim_{x \to \infty} xe^{-x} \Rightarrow -\infty.$

The graph of $y = xe^{-x}$ is shown in Fig. 3.11.

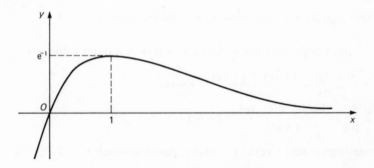

Fig. 3.11

3.9   Practical problems

The principles involved in determining the stationary points of a function, and in particular those stationary points which are maxima and minima, can be used to solve problems with a practical significance.

Such problems usually involve the following steps:

(i) The formation of an expression for the function, say f, which is to be maximised/minimised.

(ii) If this f is expressed as a function of more than one variable, then the next step is to eliminate all but one of these variables. This can usually be done by algebraic manipulation involving auxiliary conditions of the problem.

(iii) Calculation of the derivative of f with respect to the single remaining variable.

(iv) Determination of the value or values of the variable for which the derivative is zero.

(v) Test for maximum/minimum.

(vi) Calculation of the maximum/minimum value(s).

In the following examples the various stages as indicated above will be marked at the side of the working.

Example 17 Find the maximum rectangular area that can be fenced off from a rectangular field by 100 m of fencing using (a) one of the existing walls of the field, (b) two of the existing walls of the field.

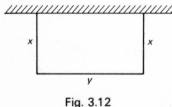

Fig. 3.12

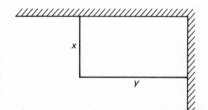

Fig. 3.13

(a) (i) Area $A = xy$, where x and y are the lengths of the sides of the rectangular area shown in Fig. 3.12.

(ii) $2x + y = 100 \Rightarrow y = 100 - 2x \Rightarrow A = x(100 - 2x)$.

(iii) $\dfrac{dA}{dx} = 100 - 4x$.

(iv) $\dfrac{dA}{dx} = 0 \Rightarrow x = 25$.

(v) $\dfrac{dA}{dx} = 4(25 - x)$

$0 < x < 25 \Rightarrow \dfrac{dA}{dx} > 0, \qquad x > 25 \Rightarrow \dfrac{dA}{dx} < 0.$

$\dfrac{dA}{dx}$ changes sign from $(+ve)$ to $(-ve)$ as x goes through 25 $\Rightarrow$ maximum area when $x = 25$.

(vi) Maximum area $= 25 \times 50 = 1250\ \text{m}^2$.

(b) (i) Area $A = xy$, where x and y are the lengths of the sides shown in Fig. 3.13.

(ii) $x + y = 100 \Rightarrow y = 100 - x \Rightarrow A = x(100 - x)$.

(iii) $\dfrac{\mathrm{d}A}{\mathrm{d}x} = 100 - 2x = 2(50 - x)$.

(iv) $\dfrac{\mathrm{d}A}{\mathrm{d}x} = 0 \Rightarrow x = 50$.

(v) $0 < x < 50 \Rightarrow \dfrac{\mathrm{d}A}{\mathrm{d}x} > 0, \qquad x > 50 \Rightarrow \dfrac{\mathrm{d}A}{\mathrm{d}x} < 0$.

$\dfrac{\mathrm{d}A}{\mathrm{d}x}$ changes sign from $(+\,\mathrm{ve})$ to $(-\,\mathrm{ve})$ as x goes through $50 \Rightarrow$ maximum area when $x = 50$.

(vi) Maximum area $= 50 \times 50 = 2500 \text{ m}^2$.

Example 18 A vertical fencing post with square section 9 cm × 9 cm is set squarely in a cubical block of concrete of side 27 cm which stands on horizontal ground. The post is supported, as shown in Fig. 3.14, by wooden tie rods which just touch the top edge of the concrete block. Find the inside length of the shortest possible support tie.

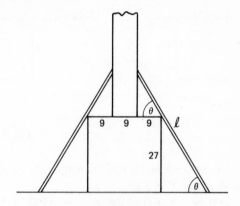

Fig. 3.14

(i) If the support makes an angle θ with the horizontal, the inside length l of the support is given by

$$l = 27 \operatorname{cosec} \theta + 9 \sec \theta,$$

(iii) $\dfrac{\mathrm{d}l}{\mathrm{d}\theta} = -27 \operatorname{cosec} \theta \cot \theta + 9 \sec \theta \tan \theta = \dfrac{-27 \cos \theta}{\sin^2 \theta} + \dfrac{9 \sin \theta}{\cos^2 \theta}$

$\qquad = \dfrac{9 \cos \theta}{\sin^2 \theta}(\tan^3 \theta - 3)$.

(iv) $\dfrac{\mathrm{d}l}{\mathrm{d}\theta} = 0 \Rightarrow \cos \theta = 0$ or $\tan^3 \theta = 3$.

$\cos \theta \neq 0$ since $0 < \theta < \pi/2 \;\Rightarrow\; \theta = \tan^{-1}\sqrt[3]{3} \approx 55{\cdot}26°$.

(v) $0 < \theta < \tan^{-1} \sqrt[3]{3} \Rightarrow \dfrac{\mathrm{d}l}{\mathrm{d}\theta} < 0,$ $\theta > \tan^{-1} \sqrt[3]{3} \Rightarrow \dfrac{\mathrm{d}l}{\mathrm{d}\theta} > 0.$

$\dfrac{\mathrm{d}l}{\mathrm{d}\theta}$ changes sign from $(-\mathrm{ve})$ to $(+\mathrm{ve})$ as θ goes through $\tan^{-1} \sqrt[3]{3}$,

$\Rightarrow$ minimum length l when $\theta = \tan^{-1} \sqrt[3]{3}$.

(vi) Minimum length $= 32{\cdot}85$ cm $+ 15{\cdot}79$ cm $= 48{\cdot}64$ cm.

Example 19   A sector is cut from a circular sheet of metal, radius r, and bent round to form a cone. Find the angle of the sector removed in order that the cone shall be of maximum volume.

Let the angle of the sector removed be $2\pi - \phi$. Let the cone be formed as shown in Fig. 3.15 – the semi-vertical angle of the cone being θ, the base radius R.

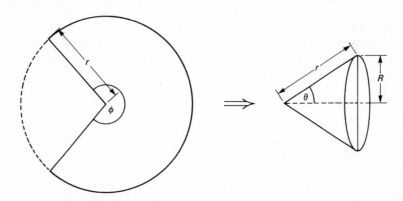

Fig. 3.15

(i) Volume of cone $V = \frac{1}{3}\pi R^2 . R \cot \theta$.

(ii) But $R = r \sin \theta$, where r is fixed,

$\Rightarrow V = \frac{1}{3}\pi r^3 \sin^3 \theta \cot \theta = \frac{1}{3}\pi r^3 \sin^2 \theta \cos \theta$.

(iii) $\dfrac{\mathrm{d}V}{\mathrm{d}\theta} = \dfrac{1}{3}\pi r^3 [2 \sin \theta \cos \theta \cos \theta + \sin^2 \theta(-\sin \theta)]$

$= \dfrac{1}{3}\pi r^3 [2 \cos^2 \theta - \sin^2 \theta] \sin \theta$.

(iv) $\dfrac{\mathrm{d}V}{\mathrm{d}\theta} = 0 \Rightarrow [2 \cos^2 \theta - \sin^2 \theta] \sin \theta = 0$

$\Rightarrow \sin \theta = 0$ or $\tan^2 \theta = 2$.

$\sin \theta = 0$ implies no cone.

$\tan^2 \theta = 2 \Rightarrow \tan \theta = \sqrt{2}$, since $0 < \theta < \pi/2$.

(v) $\dfrac{\mathrm{d}V}{\mathrm{d}\theta} = \dfrac{1}{3}\pi r^3 (2 - \tan^2 \theta) \sin \theta \cos^2 \theta$.

$$0 < \tan \theta < \sqrt{2} \Rightarrow \frac{dV}{d\theta} > 0, \qquad \tan \theta > \sqrt{2} \Rightarrow \frac{dV}{d\theta} < 0$$

$\Rightarrow \dfrac{dV}{d\theta}$ changes sign from $(+\mathrm{ve})$ to $(-\mathrm{ve})$ as $\tan \theta$ goes through $\sqrt{2}$

$\Rightarrow$ maximum volume when $\tan \theta = \sqrt{2} \Rightarrow \theta \approx 0{\cdot}9553$ radians $= 54{\cdot}73°$.

(vi) Now the arc length $r\phi$ = circumference of the base of the cone = $2\pi R$

$\Rightarrow r\phi = 2\pi R = 2\pi r \sin \theta$

$\Rightarrow \phi = 2\pi \sin \theta \approx 2\pi \sin 54{\cdot}7° \approx 5{\cdot}13$ radians $\approx 293{\cdot}9°$

$\Rightarrow$ angle of sector removed $\approx 66°$.

3.10   Geometrical significance of the second derivative

Consider the graph of a function $f(x)$ as that function changes from a minimum to a maximum and back to a minimum as shown in Fig. 3.16. In particular, consider the inclinations of the tangents to the curve at various points on the

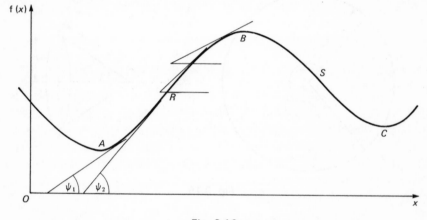

Fig. 3.16

curve between the points A and B. As we move away from A the inclination of the tangent gradually increases, i.e. $\psi_2 > \psi_1$, until the point R is reached after which the inclination ψ begins to decrease gradually to zero at B. Thus, as x increases, $f'(x)$ increases between A and R, after which $f'(x)$ decreases between R and B.

Hence for points on the curve between A and R, $f''(x) > 0$. For points on the curve between R and B, $f''(x) < 0$. At R, $f''(x) = 0$.

Similarly, between B and S, as x increases, $f'(x)$ decreases $\Rightarrow f''(x) < 0$, whilst between S and C, as x increases, $f'(x)$ increases $\Rightarrow f''(x) > 0$. At S, $f''(x) = 0$.

Points such as R and S where $f''(x) = 0$ and $f''(x)$ changes sign from $(+\mathrm{ve})$ to $(-\mathrm{ve})$ or $(-\mathrm{ve})$ to $(+\mathrm{ve})$ in passing through that point are called *points of inflexion*. They are in fact points where the gradient has a maximum or a minimum value.

Provided $f'''(x) \neq 0$, an alternative to saying $f''(x)$ changes sign from $(+ve)$ to $(-ve)$ as x increases is to say that $f'''(x) = (-ve)$. Likewise, provided $f'''(x) \neq 0$, $f''(x)$ changing sign from $(-ve)$ to $(+ve)$ as x increases implies $f'''(x) = +ve$.

Hence, $f''(x) = 0$ and $f'''(x)$ either $(+ve)$ or $(-ve)$ but not zero gives a point of inflexion; $f''(x)$ can be zero at an inflexion, but it is then necessary to investigate further and show that the first non-vanishing derivative is of an odd order, i.e. of the form $f^{(2n+1)}(x), n \geqslant 1$.

The sign of the second derivative can also often be used as an alternative test for maxima and minima.

For a maximum at B, $\dfrac{dy}{dx} = 0$ and changes sign from $(+ve)$ to $(-ve)$ in passing through B. Hence $\dfrac{dy}{dx} = 0$ and $\dfrac{d^2y}{dx^2} < 0$ gives a maximum.

Similarly, for a minimum at A, $\dfrac{dy}{dx} = 0$ and changes sign from $(-ve)$ to $(+ve)$ in passing through A. Hence, $\dfrac{dy}{dx} = 0$ and $\dfrac{d^2y}{dx^2} > 0$ gives a minimum.

It is possible to have a maximum or minimum when $\dfrac{dy}{dx} = 0$ and $\dfrac{d^2y}{dx^2} = 0$.

In this case it is necessary to show that the first non-vanishing derivative is of even order, i.e. of the form $f^{(2n)}(x)$. If this derivative is positive there is a minimum. If this derivative is negative there is a maximum.

Students often believe the test of the sign of the second derivative to be superior to that of actually testing the change of sign of the first derivative. This is not so. In fact, the more difficult the differentiation the more one should resort to testing by change of sign.

3.11 Summary

For stationary point $\dfrac{dy}{dx} = 0$.

If $\dfrac{dy}{dx}$ changes sign $(+ve)$ to $(-ve)$ or $\dfrac{d^2y}{dx^2} < 0$, maximum.

If $\dfrac{dy}{dx}$ changes sign $(-ve)$ to $(+ve)$ or $\dfrac{d^2y}{dx^2} > 0$, minimum.

If $\dfrac{dy}{dx}$ does not change sign there is a point of inflexion with a horizontal tangent.

If $\dfrac{d^2y}{dx^2} = 0$ and $\dfrac{d^3y}{dx^3} \neq 0$, point of inflexion (with a horizontal tangent if $\dfrac{dy}{dx} = 0$ also).

Example 20 Find the stationary points and the points of inflexion on the curve $y = x^3 - 6x^2 + 9x + 6$. Sketch the curve.

$$y = x^3 - 6x^2 + 9x + 6.$$

$$\frac{dy}{dx} = 3x^2 - 12x + 9, \quad \frac{d^2y}{dx^2} = 6x - 12.$$

For stationary points, $\dfrac{dy}{dx} = 0 \Rightarrow 3x^2 - 12x + 9 = 0 = 3(x - 1)(x - 3)$

$$\Rightarrow x = 1 \text{ or } 3.$$

When $x = 1, \dfrac{d^2y}{dx^2} = 6 - 12 = -6 < 0 \Rightarrow$ maximum when $x = 1, y = 10$.

When $x = 3, \dfrac{d^2y}{dx^2} = 18 - 12 = 6 > 0 \Rightarrow$ minimum when $x = 3, y = 6$.

For points of inflexion,

$$\frac{d^2y}{dx^2} = 0 \Rightarrow 6(x - 2) = 0 \Rightarrow x = 2,$$

$$\frac{d^3y}{dx^3} = 6 > 0 \quad \Rightarrow \text{at } x = 2, \frac{d^3y}{dx^3} > 0$$

$\Rightarrow$ point of inflexion at (2, 8).

$$x = 0, y = 6; \quad x \to +\infty, y \to +\infty; \quad x \to -\infty, y \to -\infty$$

$\Rightarrow$ curve is as shown in Fig. 3.17.

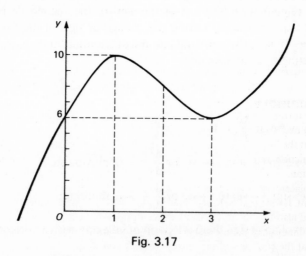

Fig. 3.17

Example 21   By considering the stationary values of $f(x) = x^3 - 3px^2 + 4q$, where p, q are real positive constants, show that the equation $f(x) = 0$ has three real distinct roots if $p^3 > q$.

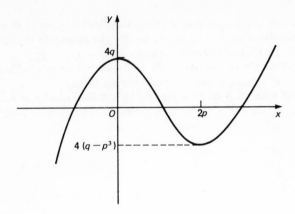

Fig. 3.18

$$f(x) = x^3 - 3px^2 + 4q \Rightarrow f'(x) = 3x^2 - 6px.$$

$$f'(x) = 0 \Rightarrow 3x(x - 2p) = 0 \Rightarrow x = 0 \text{ or } 2p.$$

$f''(x) = 6x - 6p \Rightarrow f''(0) = -6p = -\text{ve} \Rightarrow f(x)$ has a maximum value of $4q$ when $x = 0$.

$f''(2p) = 12p - 6p = +\text{ve} \Rightarrow f(x)$ has a minimum value of $8p^3 - 12p^3 + 4q$, or $4(q - p^3)$, when $x = 2p$. If $p^3 > q$ the minimum value $4(q - p^3)$ is negative and the curve $y = x^3 - 3px^2 + 4q$ is shown in Fig. 3.18. The curve crosses the x-axis in three distinct points. Hence, for p and q real positive constants and $p^3 > q$, the equation $f(x) = 0$ has three distinct roots.

Exercise 3.11

1 Find the maximum and minimum ordinates on the curve $y = x^3 + x^2$.
2 If $y\sqrt{3} = x\sqrt{(x + 1)}$, prove that y has a minimum value of $-2/9$ when $x = -2/3$. Sketch the curves (i) $y\sqrt{3} = x\sqrt{(x + 1)}$, (ii) $3y^2 = x^2(x + 1)$.
3 Find the turning points on the curve $y = \cos x + 2 \cos \frac{1}{2}x$ for $0 \leqslant x \leqslant 2\pi$. Sketch the curve over this range.
4 Show that the function $y = e^{-x}/x$ has a maximum at $x = -1$. Consider the behaviour of the function near $x = 0$, and as $x \to \pm\infty$, and illustrate by drawing a graph of the function. (AEB)
5 The displacement x m of a particle at time t s is given by $x = Ce^{-3t}(2t^2 + t)$, C constant. If the initial velocity of the particle is 3 m s^{-1}, determine the initial acceleration. Find also the maximum displacement of the particle.
6 The coordinates of a point on a curve are given by the equations $x = \cos^3 t, y = \sin^3 t$. Prove that the equation of the tangent to the curve at the point t is $x \sin t + y \cos t = \sin t \cos t$. Find the perimeter P of the triangle formed by this tangent and the axes, and prove that the maximum value of P is $1 + \sqrt{2}$.
7 The function $f(x)$, where $f(x) = \dfrac{ax + b}{x(x + 2)}$, has a stationary point at $(1, -2)$. Find the constants a and b, and determine the nature of this stationary point. Hence sketch the curve $y = f(x)$.

8 Show that the curve $xy = \ln(1/x)$ passes throught the point $(1, 0)$ and that y has a minimum value when $x = $ e. Show also that the tangent to the curve at the point where $x = \sqrt{e}$ passes through the origin.

9 A right circular cone is carved out of a solid sphere of volume V. Show that the minimum amount of material that must be wasted is $19V/27$.   (AEB)

10 Figure 3.19 shows a pole AB supported by a tie-bar which just passes over a wall 6 m high, distant 8 m from the pole. Calculate the minimum length of the tie-bar required.

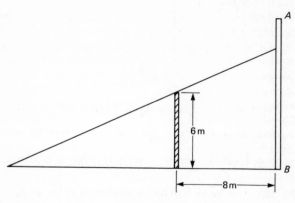

Fig. 3.19

11 Three boards, each of length l and width a, are used to construct the horizontal bottom and sloping sides of an open water trough of length l. At what angle to the vertical should the sides be placed in order that the trough may have the greatest volume? Show that this volume is $3\sqrt{3a^2 l}/4$.

12 Show that the function $3x + \sin x - 8 \sin \frac{1}{2}x$ is always positive for positive values of x and find the values of x corresponding to which there are points of inflexion on the graph of the function.

13 Find the largest and smallest values of the function $e^{-2x}(4x^2 - 2x + 1)$ in the range $0 \leqslant x \leqslant 2$.

14 Find the maximum and minimum values of the expression $x/(1 + x^2)$. Sketch the curve $y = x/(1 + x^2)$.

15 The total cost per hour of running a ship while on a voyage is £$(45 + \frac{1}{5}v^2)$, where v knots is the constant speed for the voyage. If the ship makes a voyage of 3000 sea-miles, find the most economical speed and the total cost of the voyage at this speed. [1 knot = 1 sea-mile per hour.]   (L)

16 (i) Find the maximum and minimum values of the function $(2 \sin x + \sin 2x)$ in the interval $0 \leqslant x \leqslant 2\pi$, and sketch the graph of this function in this interval.

(ii) Find the stationary values of the function

$$3e^{3x} - 9e^{2x} + 8e^x$$

and determine their nature.   (L)

17 By considering the stationary values of the expression $f(x)$, where $f(x) = x^3 + px + q$, $p > 0, q > 0$, or otherwise, show that the equation $f(x) = 0$ has precisely one negative root and no positive root.

18 A window consists of a rectangle of width $2x$ and height a, surmounted by a semicircle of diameter $2x$. If the perimeter of the window is P, show that the area of the window is given by the formula

$$A = Px - 2x^2 - \tfrac{1}{2}\pi x^2.$$

If x varies and P is constant, find, in terms of P, the greatest possible area of the window. (L)

19 A rectangle $ABCD$ is inscribed in an equilateral triangle PQR of side $2a$, the points A and B lying on QR, C lying on RP and D on PQ. Find the length of AB for which the area of the rectangle is a maximum.

20 The intensity of illumination of an element of a plane area varies inversely as the square of the distance r of the element from the source, S, of light and directly as the cosine of the angle between the normal to the element and the line joining the element to S. Find at what height above the centre of a circular disc, of radius a, the source S should be placed so that the intensity of illumination at the circumference of the circle should be greatest. (L)

21 A manufacturer asks for a cylindrical tub to be constructed to contain a volume of 1000 cm³. The tub is to be open at the top and is to be made of material 1 cm in thickness. If the amount of material used is to be a minimum, show that the internal radius and the internal height are each equal to $10/\sqrt[3]{\pi}$ cm. (L)

22 A right circular cone of semi-vertical angle $\tfrac{1}{2}\theta$ is inscribed in a sphere of radius a. Show that the volume of the cone is V, where

$$V = \frac{1}{3}\pi a^3 \sin^2 \theta (1 + \cos \theta).$$

Show that, as θ varies, the ratio of the maximum volume of the cone to the volume of the sphere is 8/27.

23 A particle moves along the x-axis so that at time t its distance x from the origin O is given by

$$x = t^3 - 6t^2 + 15t.$$

Show that the velocity is always positive, and find its least value. Sketch graphs of $\dfrac{dx}{dt}$ and x. Indicate clearly on the graph of x the point corresponding to the least velocity. (L)

24 $ABCD$ is a rectangle in which $AB = 9$ cm and $BC = 4$ cm. A variable line through B meets DA produced at P and DC produced at Q. Find an expression for the area of the triangle PDQ in terms of the angle QPD, and hence find the minimum area of the triangle.

Answers

Exercise 1.4

1 $6x$
2 $14x + 6x^{-3}$
3 $-6(1 - 3t)$
4 $-2 - 2x$
5 $x^{-1/2} - 9x^{1/2} + 28x^{5/2}$
6 $2t^{1/2} \cos t + t^{-1/2} \sin t$
7 $\sec \theta \tan \theta$
8 $-\operatorname{cosec}^2 v$
9 $e^x(\sin x + \cos x)$
10 $x^{-1} - 2 \ln x - 2$
11 $-4(1 + 2x)^{-2}$
12 $\frac{1}{2}x^{-1/2} \cdot (1 + \sqrt{x})^{-2}$
13 $7e^x(2 - e^x)^{-2}$
14 0
15 $x \sin 2x + x^2 \cos 2x$
16 $1 - 10x + 18x^2$
17 $2x(1 - x^2)^{-2}$
18 $\theta^{-1} \cos \theta - \theta^{-2} \sin \theta$
19 $2 \cos t(1 - \sin t)^{-2}$
20 $\sec u \tan u$
21 $-2(2 + x)^{-3}$.

Exercise 1.8

1 $12(3x + 2)^3$
2 $\frac{5}{2}x^{3/2} + \frac{3}{2}x^{1/2} - x^{-1/2}$
3 $10(2 - 5u)^{-3}$
4 $-\frac{1}{3}(3 - x)^{-2/3}$
5 $\frac{7}{2}(3 - 7x)^{-3/2}$
6 $(1 + t)^{-2}$
7 $(3x + 1)(3x^2 + 2x - 5)^{-1/2}$
8 $\frac{1}{2}(5 + 2x)(3 - 5x - x^2)^{-3/2}$
9 $\frac{1}{2}u^{-1/2}(1 - u)^{-3/2}$
10 $(3u - 2)u^{-3}(1 - 2u)^{-1/2}$
11 $11(5 - 2x)^{-2}$
12 $(3t^2 - 2t + 2)(3t - 1)^{-2}$
13 $\frac{1}{3} \cos (\theta/3)$
14 $-2 \operatorname{cosec}^2 2x$
15 $\frac{1}{3}\sin^{-2/3}t \cos t$
16 $2 \sin 4x$
17 $\theta^2(3 \cos \theta - \theta \sin \theta)$
18 $-4 \cot 4x \operatorname{cosec} 4x$
19 $\sin x \cos^2 x(2 \cos^2 x - 3 \sin^2 x)$
20 $12 \sec^2 \theta(1 + 3 \tan \theta)^3$
21 $7 \cos x(4 + 3 \sin x)^{-2}$

22 $-\cos \theta \sin \theta(2 + \cos \theta)(1 + \cos \theta)^{-2}$
23 $2e^{2t}(\tan 2t + \sec^2 2t)$
24 $\sec^2 x$
25 $5e^{5x}$
26 $(5 - 2t)e^{5t - t^2}$
27 $\cos \theta \, e^{\sin \theta}$
28 $4 \sin 2\theta \, e^{-2 \cos 2\theta}$
29 $2e^{2x}(x^{-2} - x^{-3})$
30 $-e^{-3x}(3 \cos 2x + 2 \sin 2x)$
31 $-2 \, e^{3-2t}$
32 $2e^{2x} - 2e^{-2x}$
33 $\dfrac{2}{2x - 1}$
34 $\dfrac{-2u}{1 - u^2}$
35 $-\dfrac{1}{2(1 - x)}$
36 $\dfrac{1}{x^2}(1 - \ln x)$
37 $(1 - 4x)(x - 2x^2)^{-1}$
38 $-\tan 2x$
39 $e^{2t}(2 \ln 4t + 1/t)$
40 $-3 \tan 3x + 3 \cos 3x(2 - \sin 3x)^{-1}$.

Exercise 2.1

1 x/y
2 $-9x/(4y)$
3 $(2 - x)/(y + 3)$
4 $(12x^3 + 8xy^2)/(21y^2 - 8x^2 y)$
5 $\dfrac{(3x^2 - 4x^3 - 4xy^2)}{(4x^2 y + 4y^3 - 3y^2)}$
6 $y(2x^2 - 1)/[x(2y^2 - 1)]$
7 $\dfrac{[2y^2 \cos 2x - 6xy + y \sin (xy)]}{[3x^2 - 2y \sin 2x - x \sin (xy)]}$

Exercise 2.7

1 $(x^{-3} \sin 2x - x^{-2} \cos 2x - 3ye^{3x})e^{-3x}$
4 -6
5 $(\cos t + \sin t)/(\cos t - \sin t)$
6 1
10 $(1 + xy - y^3)/(1 + xy)^3$
11 ± 4
13 $-2 \sin x$

14 (i) $\dfrac{2x}{\sqrt{(1-x^4)}}$, (ii) $\dfrac{-1}{t^2-2t+2}$,

(iii) $\dfrac{1}{2x\sqrt{(x-1)}}$, (iv) -1,

(v) $\dfrac{-1}{(1+x)\sqrt{(2x+x^2)}}$,

(vi) $\dfrac{e^x(\sin x + \cos x)}{\sqrt{(1-e^{2x}\sin^2 x)}}$

15 $\dfrac{-2}{\sqrt{(2-x^2)}}$.

Exercise 3.2
1 $2y = 3x - 1, 3y + 2x = 18$
2 $\sqrt{2}y = x + 3, \sqrt{2}y + x + 3 = 0, 4$
6 $3y = 4x - 2, (\tfrac{1}{3}, -\tfrac{2}{9})$
7 $a = 1, b = -6, c = 9$
8 $3y = 4x - 1, -1/9$
9 $(1+x)^2(1-2x)/y, (\tfrac{1}{2}, \pm 3\sqrt{3}/4),$
$(1, 0).$

Exercise 3.3
1 0·48
2 0·51
3 1·557
4 $-0·490$
6 1·2788
7 1·5053
8 2·48

Exercise 3.4
1 8·2 cm per minute
2 $5/\sqrt{3}$ cm s^{-1}
3 $3\tfrac{1}{3}$ cm s^{-1}
4 5·21 cm s^{-1}
5 $k = -1, n = 4/3, a = 3/2$
6 $-f/16$
7 $e^{-2t}(8t - 2 - 8t^2), 2/(1 + 4t^2)$

8 -2
9 $4 \text{ m}^2 \text{ s}^{-1}, 5 \text{ m}$

Exercise 3.6
1 12, 12·006
2 2·00521
3 150·4
5 7% too large
6 2·5% too large
7 0·023
8 2·2% too large.

Exercise 3.7
4 $x \ln(1 + x)$

Exercise 3.11
1 Min 0, Max 4/27.
3 $(0, 3)$Max, $(4\pi/3, -3/2)$Min, $(2\pi, -1)$Max
5 $-6 \text{ m s}^{-2}, 3e^{-3/2}$ m
6 $1 + \sin t + \cos t$
7 $a = -8, b = 2$, Min.
10 19·7 m.
11 30°
12 $2n\pi$
13 1, 0·238
14 0·5, $-0·5$
15 15 knots, £18 000
16 (i) Max. $3\sqrt{3}/2$, Min. $-3\sqrt{3}/2$,
(ii) Max. $2\tfrac{2}{9}$, Min. $1\tfrac{7}{9}$
18 $P^2/2(4 + \pi)$
19 a
20 $a/\sqrt{2}$
23 3
24 $\tfrac{1}{2}(72 + 16 \tan\theta + 81 \cot\theta)$ cm^2, 72 cm^2

Index